THE STORY OF AMERICA'S HORSES

THE STORY OF
AMERICA'S HORSES

LOUIS TAYLOR

Illustrated by Lorence Bjorklund

THE WORLD PUBLISHING COMPANY

CLEVELAND AND NEW YORK

Published by The World Publishing Company
2231 West 110th Street, Cleveland, Ohio 44102
Published simultaneously in Canada by
Nelson, Foster & Scott Ltd.
Library of Congress catalog card number: 68–28482

THE STORY OF AMERICA'S HORSES

Spanish Horses Come to the New World

Christopher Columbus lay dying in chains in a Spanish prison as the news of gold in the New World he had discovered was flying across Spain like a hurricane. Everybody wanted gold. But the wealthy feared leaving their comfortable palaces for a perilous sea voyage to a land of swamps, mountains, and alligator-infested rivers. Few of the venturesome and brave had enough money to buy a ship and slaves and horses for a gold hunt. Horses they had to have, for no Spaniard would ever think of journeying any distance except on horseback.

The man who was most respected in Spain was the man whose horse moved as if he were part of his rider's body. By the lightest touch of hand or heel, Spanish horsemen could hurl their mounts forward like bullets, stop them on their haunches with ironshod forefeet in air, pivot them on one hind foot, skip them sidewise, or make them perform a dance step. If only they could get some horses to the New

World, the Spaniards felt sure that no swamp, mountain, river, beast, or savage could stop them; and they could find gold.

In 1518 one of the best of Spanish horsemen, Hernando Cortez, and a few staunch friends managed to procure ships, horses, slaves, and weapons for an expedition. They called themselves *conquistadores*, which is the Spanish word for "conquerors." Their purpose was to conquer the land of gold, the land of the Aztecs and Mayas, for their king.

Their horses terrified the Indians of Mexico when the Spaniards reached the New World the next year. The Indians thought the conquistadors were strange gods, rushing at them on four legs. The Spaniards slaughtered many of the terror-stricken Indians but soon they realized that they could use the Indians as guides. In getting food and in building bridges, the Indians proved to be very useful.

In 1525 at Lake Petén in Guatemala, the black stallion El Morzillo, favorite mount of Cortez, so badly injured a foot that he could not travel. He was left behind in the care of an Indian chief. With great respect the chief had received the strange animal and promised to care for him. We know nothing more about El Morzillo's life.

In 1697, almost 150 years after Cortez left El Morzillo with the Indian chief, another Spanish expedition under the leader Martin de Ursua approached Lake Petén. The Indians went wild with excitement upon seeing the horses. One Indian, named Iquin, got down on his hands and knees, jumped about and neighed like a horse. A Franciscan priest traveling with the Ursua expedition found that the Indians had built a great idol, the image of a big black horse. So we know that the horses of Spain, in addition to being the first ever seen by humans on the continent of North America, were the first and only horses on this continent to become sacred.

Poor El Morzillo died and became a god at Lake Petén, leaving no offspring. But other Spanish horses were more fortunate. Left behind when crippled or lost in battle, they found the grass ranges of Mexico to be a good home. Horses escaping from explorers who followed Cortez joined them and soon there were large bands of horses roaming the country. When the Indians were subdued (the Spaniards said "reduced"), cattle were brought over from Spain and the first cattle ranching was started on the North American continent. The bands of horses descended from the mounts of the conquistadors were the source of cow ponies used to tend the cattle.

So it was that the first cowboys in North America rode horses that were descended from those of the Spanish conquistadors. The first horse breeding in the United States was started with that same stock, for on April 20, 1598, Juan de Oñate drove into the Rio Grande River, from the south bank, with eighty-three wagons and seven thousand horses, cattle, and sheep. He crossed the river near what is now El Paso, Texas. Oñate became so prosperous that in ten years he proclaimed himself governor of the Spanish colony of New Mexico and established the capital of the colony at Santa Fe. Many thousands of horses, donkeys, mules, and cattle were soon grazing on the grassy ranges of what is now Texas and New Mexico.

Though these horses were descended from the mounts of the conquistadors, they did not look exactly like their ancestors. Horses of the conquistadors were of Arabian and North African blood. Arabians, the most beautiful horses in the world, had small heads with large, deerlike eyes, small delicate noses, and fine ears, pricked forward and set close together. Their necks were arched and their tails were set high and carried like flags when they ran. The North African horses, called Barbs, were not as pretty and were a little larger than the Arabians. They were inclined to be Roman-nosed, and their tails were set low. The best Spanish horses, called Andalusians, were as beautiful as the Arabians but were a little larger and sturdier because of their Barb blood.

Having run wild for several generations without controlled breeding, the horses descended from the Spanish mounts of the conquistadors were smaller than their ancestors and not as pretty, but they were tough and quick. They were of all colors. Most of them were solid bay, brown, chestnut, or black; for Arabian horses are always of solid color—never spotted or speckled. But some of the sturdy, little New Mexico horses took their colors from their Barb ancestors. They were pinto (or paint), speckled like the Appaloosas or dun with zebralike stripes on their upper legs, for such color patterns occurred among North African horses.

Horses Go North—and East

The success of the Spaniards did not last. By 1680, when the Spaniards' horse population had grown to over six thousand head, the Pueblo Indians of the American Southwest had taken all the abuse they could stand from their conquerors. They teamed up with the Navajos and the Apaches, killed four hundred Spaniards, and looted all the Spanish corrals. The Spaniards abandoned Santa Fe, taking with them what little livestock they could lay their hands on. Then the Indian tribes began fighting among themselves, stealing horses from one another. The Ute Indians came down from the north—the state of Utah gets its name from them—and stole from the Apaches. The Pawnees from the Platte River country of Nebraska stole horses from the

Utes. By 1738, the Mandan Indians of Dakota had horses. Earlier than that, the Pawnees of the Arkansas River country had from six thousand to eight thousand horses and were using leather breastplates and other horse gear in imitation of the Spaniards. By 1750, Spanish horses were being sold by Indians to trappers in the Hudson Bay country of Canada. The Cayuse Indians of western Washington

and Oregon had so many horses that the word "cayuse" soon became the name used all over the Northwest for an Indian horse.

The Indian took the Spanish horse north, and he also took it east. The Caddo Indians of Louisiana in 1689, as reported by a French explorer, rode horses equipped with Spanish saddles and bridles. These horses carried the brands of New Mexico. This fact takes us to a mystery about a breed of American horses that has never been solved.

The Mystery of the Chickasaws

About the time the Indians drove the first Spanish colonists out of New Mexico, plantation owners of Maryland and Virginia were complaining about bands of wild horses that were grazing in their grain fields. And plantation owners farther south were talking about the fine horses owned by the Indians of South Carolina and Georgia. Descendants of these horses survive today and they are still known in their native territory as Chickasaw horses. They are small, seldom over four and a half feet tall at the top of their shoulders.

All the old written accounts say that the Chickasaws were pretty horses, suitable for both riding and heavy work in harness. The quality of prettiness suggests that they might have come from the best Spanish stock, but no Spanish horse ever looked suitable for heavy work in harness. Some men who have studied the matter carefully claim that they must have descended from the horses of the Spanish explorers of Florida. Other equally careful men (among them J. Frank Dobie, who grew up on a Texas ranch and became a scholar respected in this country and abroad) say that these little horses could not have descended from Spanish horses brought to southeastern North America because none of those horses survived.

The Indians whom Cortez found in his conquest of Mexico feared horses. They even made a god of one of them. But the Indians of Florida hated horses and hunted them down and slaughtered them wherever they could be found. These Indians were "more pleased to kill one horse than four cavaliers," Dobie tells us.

The explorer Hernando de Soto was so impressed by the powerful bows of the Indians that he wrote a document, signed by himself and a notary, telling of an Indian arrow that "went clean through the largest and fattest horse in camp and stuck in the ground on the other side." De Soto, the proudest and best equipped of all the explorers of Florida, landed on the mainland in 1539 with about 250

horses. In three years he was dead, leaving only a few of
his men. He had fought Indians and pushed into the New
World as far as the Mississippi valley. The survivors of his
party embarked on the Mississippi River for home. For
twelve days, with their four or five remaining horses aboard,
they sailed down the Mississippi toward the Gulf of Mexico.
On the twelfth day, several miles above the river's mouth,
they took the horses off the boat to graze. Indians attacked.
The Spaniards escaped to their boat and saw the horses
being slaughtered by the Indians.

Panfilo de Narvaes, another gallant Spaniard, killed all

the remaining horses but one, an escapee, before he left the mainland.

Even if a few horses of the Spanish searchers for the Seven Cities of Cibola and the Fountain of Youth did survive as foundation stock for the Chickasaw horses, there was a better supply of horses for the Indians to draw from in the grasslands to the north. Horses strayed from every settlement on the eastern coast and by 1680 wild bands were to be found in every wooded grassy area where horses could hide from human pursuit.

Whatever the secret of the origin of the Chickasaw horses, they were bartered for by colonists and traded among the Indians, so they soon became an important part of American horse blood. But they were not taken to the West and were not ancestors of the western cow ponies.

North European Horses Come to America

Before there were any people in North America or South America, prehistoric horses roamed the plains and pampas, but they disappeared before the ancestors of the Indians reached America from Asia. The Spaniards brought the first horses back to America, but it was from England and from Holland and France that the first horses to found an American breed came. The first English horses were, of course, brought over by the colonists.

The colonists called Pilgrims or Separatists because they had separated from the Church of England lived for a time in Holland; but on September 16, 1620, they set sail for America from Plymouth, England. Without horses and with few tools, the first year in America was one of great hardship and struggle for the Pilgrims. Half their number died. So grateful to God were the remainder for surviving that first terrible year, they had a day of thanksgiving with a great dinner made of the strange foods of their new land—cranberries, potatoes, and a large wild bird the Indians had taught them to hunt. They called the bird a turkey because the color and shape of its head suggested a hook-nosed man wearing a red fez—a hat worn by the men of Turkey at that time.

The survival of the Pilgrims in the new land encouraged many religious groups to seek freedom there. During the year 1630, more than a thousand Puritans sailed into Massachussetts Bay. Soon small towns were scattered along the coast—Dorchester, Medford, Watertown, Roxbury, Lynn, and others. England encouraged such settlement and, by forbidding all but English ships to carry supplies to the New World, the king collected taxes from the merchants selling goods to the colonists.

The Pilgrims, and all the other early colonists so badly needed supplies from England that they paid whatever was asked to get them. They needed cattle, sheep, hogs, and chickens, for there were none of these in the new land when the Pilgrims came. And the New Englanders desperately needed horses. In 1650 horses imported from the Old World to the New had to be hardy; the voyage across the stormy Atlantic took two months.

Because the king had forbidden any but English ships to trade with colonists, horses for shipment to the colonies had to be selected from those available in Great Britain and Ireland.

The finest and most expensive horses in England were owned by the lords and the king. They were the ones used only inside the palaces and in the great halls which were richly decorated with mirrors, crystal, and tapestries. These horses were taught to trot with high steps without moving forward, and jump straight up in the air from a standstill. They were taught other movements much like dance steps. It was almost as fashionable for the lords and ladies to learn to ride these horses as it is today to learn the latest dance steps. These riding-hall horses, which were called *manège* horses, had chests like pouter pigeons and they were shaped much like the Shetland ponies we see today. Of course they were much larger than ponies.

The large draft horses used on the farms in Great Britain were called Great Horses. They were the descendants of

the huge mounts of the armored knights of the days of
chivalry. They were also the ancestors of the big horses
called Clydesdales and Shires.

Still another kind of horse used in Great Britain and
Ireland was the easy-riding horse used by common folk.
It was not as pretty as the manège horse, and not as large
—about halfway in size between a Shetland pony and the

full-size saddle horse of today. But small as they were, they were very tough, and they moved so easily that a **rider** could carry a glass full of water without spilling a drop. Some of the prettiest of these easy-gaited horses were kept by the nobles and by the king. They were used mostly by women and were called palfreys. But even a lord would ride a palfrey when he needed a horse to ride outside the riding hall.

The men who selected horses for shipment to America found the manège horses too expensive. The Great Horses were too large to transport in the holds of the sailing vessels of that day. Also, they were less suited to withstand the lurching and tossing of a ship in a storm than were the smaller easy-riding horses. So it was the small, common riding horse that was sent over to America.

Early Colonial Horses

Life in the early colonies was hard. It took rugged people and tough horses to survive. The first horses imported to

Plymouth, Virginia, and other English colonies stood between fifty and fifty-six inches high at the top of their shoulders, or as horsemen would say, thirteen to fourteen hands. A hand is equal to four inches, or the breadth of a human hand. The heads of these horses were not as pretty as those we see today on Arabian horses. Their eyes were nearer the tops of their heads and their noses were longer and broader. Also their necks were shorter than those of the American Saddle Horses seen in horse shows or parades today, and they were not arched as prettily. They looked as if they were "put on upside down," as one

modern horseman says. That is, instead of being arched like those of beautiful horses today, they looked more like those of sheep. Horsemen call such necks "ewe-necks." The backs of the early colonial horses were longer than those of good riding horses today, and their hips were more sloping and shorter. But their legs were sturdy and their feet were tough. These little horses were not pretty, but they were hardy and they could carry their rider easily over any kind of trail or rough ground.

The Gaits

Most American horses today move very differently from the common riding horse of colonial days. They walk, trot, and gallop. When the gallop is slowed down and made easy for the rider by training, we call it a canter. When a horse walks, he strikes the ground with one foot at a time. The sound he makes when he walks on dry ground makes us think of four-four time in music. We can count the steps: "one, two, three, four."

When a horse trots, his feet strike the ground in pairs. The left front foot and right hind foot strike at the same time. So do his right front foot and left hind foot. The trot is like two-four time in music. We can count the hoofbeats: "one, two; one, two."

The gallop or canter is more complicated. If a horse starts to gallop with his left hind foot, it strikes the ground and is followed by a diagonal pair, the right hind and left front feet, which strike the ground simultaneously. Then the right front foot strikes the ground. All this makes the gallop sound like three-four time in music. We count the hoofbeats: "one, two, three; one, two, three."

The common riding horse did not trot at all. This seems strange to us. The trot is, for us, a very important gait. It is the one most used by cowboys when they want to ride faster than a walk, except for those short dashes when they have to rope a cow or calf. The trot was the gait most used by the cavalry on the march when a walk was not fast enough.

Today we can use the trot, the gait that common horses of colonial days did not do, because we have learned a good deal about riding. But people who are not skillful riders find the trot very bumpy and uncomfortable.

In England until the seventeenth century, there were few wheeled vehicles for transportation. There were rude carts and farm wagons, but nothing for comfortable transportation. There was not a single stagecoach line in England or a decent road for one until 1640, when the first lines began. Because of this, whenever one wanted to travel, whether across town or across the country, he had to ride a horse. Most busy people did not have time to learn to ride well enough to sit comfortably on a trotting horse. In those days a horse that trotted was called a "boneshaker" and was considered fit only for servants to ride or for use as a pack animal. Of course the fancy horses in the great

Trot

Pace

Gallop

riding halls trotted, but they were never used for transportation. The gallop, then as now, was seldom used. It was the gait for emergency speed or for foolish harum-scarums who had no regard for their horses. Both the gallop and canter soon cripple a horse if used much on hard ground or rough roads.

The gaits of the early English, Irish, and colonial horses were the ones we call today the *fox trot,* the *amble,* the *running walk,* and the *rack* or *single-foot.* In those early days, all these gaits were usually called by one name, the *pace.* This is very confusing to us and has led to some mistakes by historical writers because today we use the word "pace" as the name of a very different gait. It is the gait used by some of our fast, modern harness-race horses, horses that can pace a mile in considerably less than two minutes pulling a man in a wheeled vehicle. The modern pace is a two-beat gait that sounds like the trot. It is in two-four time, and can be counted, "one, two; one, two; one, two." However, though the feet strike the ground in pairs as in the trot, it is the pair of feet on the same side that work together. The left front and left hind feet strike the ground at the same time. So do the right front and right hind, of course. This gait, performed at high speed, is a modern development and has little to do with the easy gaits of the colonial saddler, though he too was called a "pacer."

The little colonial horse in his fox trot, single-foot, or other easy gait never struck the ground with two feet simultaneously, though in each gait except in the single-foot and the running walk his feet worked in pairs and one foot of each pair would strike the ground slightly before its mate did. The rhythm was like that of syncopated music. To such gaits it is easy to sing, "Come *on* a-*long,* come *on* a-*long.*" The single-foot and the running walk are four-beat gaits like the walk, but they are, of course, faster.

The Narragansetts and the Dutch

The little easy-gaited colonial horses carried the Virginia planters from town to plantation and the Puritans from town to farm. They carried the preachers to church and the doctors and nurses to tend the sick. They carried the young and restless men pushing through trackless wilderness to find new land beyond the clearings. They forded the streams and floundered through the snowdrifts in winter.

As the colonies grew, settlers began to raise horses. Any owner of a stallion whose colts had easy gaits and more size than average was very fortunate. His neighbors paid for their mares to have colts by the stallion. Word spread from Canada that pacers, larger than the little horses of New England, had been imported. Now and then a colonist, braver than the rest and with a little more money in his pocket than most, would make the long and dangerous trip north and bring back a Canadian Pacer. One colonist was said to have covered more than ninety miles on the last day of his trip from Canada to the colony by Narragansett Bay. The fame of a new breed of horse, the Narragansett Pacer, became so great that traders bringing rum and sugar cane to New England from the British colonies in the West Indies loaded their ships with them before they set sail for home. West Indian companies soon had agents in the region of Narragansett Bay scouting for these sorrel and bay pacers, willing to purchase them at any price demanded. The Narragansett Pacers were a little larger than the colonial saddlers. Their movement was graceful. They were more beautiful and of greater endurance than most horses. They were undoubtedly the first breed of horse ever developed in America and the only one that has completely disappeared; for disappear they did. Their fame spread so fast and so far that export prices for them soared and they all left our shores.

The only early colonial horses that were not easy-gaited were those imported by the Dutch settlers who founded New Amsterdam in 1624. These horses had thick bodies with short necks and short, stocky legs. Their gaits were limited to the walk, trot, and gallop. The Dutch settlers liked these horses because they were the kind they had used on their farms in Holland.

In 1664, when the British captured New Amsterdam and put its eight hundred inhabitants under British rule, the place was renamed New York. Soon the easy-riding horses became more popular in New York than the chunky, hard-riding Dutch horses. Some of the Dutch stock was mated with the horses of the English colonists. This addition of a little Dutch blood caused some colonial horses to be stockier than before.

Colonial Pacers

While New England was raising horses from the stock of
the easy-riding kind, changes were taking place in England
that would revolutionize horse breeding. In 1660, following the Puritan Revolution, Charles II returned from exile
in France. He was an enthusiastic horseman and set up
the finest breeding establishment England had ever known.
His good friend, the Duke of Newcastle, was one of the most
famous horsemen of all time. He helped the king select a
band of mares, since called the "Royal Mares," some of
which were imported and some picked from native English
stock. The Duke of Newcastle also organized horse racing
in England. The Royal Mares he helped to select were to
found a new breed of horse called the "Thoroughbred,"
which will be discussed in greater detail later in this book.

Something else happened to change the style of horses
in England. New roads were built, and by 1680, stagecoach
travel became an important part of life. Soon wheeled

vehicles were becoming the fashionable means of transportation. This meant that horseback riding was no longer necessary for people who were not skilled riders. They could ride in vehicles horses pulled.

It is much easier for a horse to pull a buggy or carriage if he pushes the ground under him with two feet at a time than if he uses his feet one at a time. So the trot became popular for transportation. And the gallop, the fastest gait a horse has, became the only gait used on the new race tracks. In 1600 it was difficult to find—outside the riding halls—a good horse that trotted; in 1700 it was equally difficult to find one that did not trot.

All the best horse breeders in England began raising Thoroughbreds—horses whose parents, grandparents, or great-grandparents were colts from the Royal Mares. New Englanders continued to breed and improve horses of the old style. Until after the American Revolution, horses were one of the leading exports of New England, going principally to the West Indies, to Virginia, and to England. In the early 1700s Narragansett led America in horse breeding, but there were other families, or breeds, of horses developed that were almost as famous as the Narragansetts and as equally sought after by exporters. One of them was called the Clark Horse. This family of excellent little horses was bred by Doctor John Clark of Plymouth, an ancestor of Paul Revere's landlord. It is not surprising that a doctor developed good horses, for the poor roads and long dis-

tances he had to travel made it necessary for him to have them.

Good horses they were, indeed. A rector of the Narragansett church in 1750 said of the Clark Horse, "They are remarkable for fleetness and swift pacing, and I have seen one of them pace a mile in a little more than two minutes and a good deal less than three." Remember the pace that the rector was talking about was not the pace of the modern race horse. Today, what we call a pace is an artificial gait, not a natural one like that of the colonial horses. The modern pacer is kept in his gait by straps called hopples around his legs.

The rector had a "pacer" which he sometimes rode fifty or sixty miles in a day over bad roads. He said that the best of the horses of his locality could go one hundred miles in a day without tiring either the horse or rider.

Of course these little horses that were so fleet and so tireless were also very lively. Late in the 1600s, a Hollander named Rip Van Dam bought one of them for export to New York. After some difficulty, it was loaded on a sloop for shipment. However, no sooner was the animal loaded than it jumped overboard and swam ashore. Van Dam eventually received the horse at his home in New York. In a letter he wrote:

> "He was no beauty, although so high priced, save in his legs. He always plays and acts and never will stand still. He will take a glass of wine, beer or cyder."

One of the first horses of the new English breed, the Thoroughbred, to be seen in the colonies was a British colonel's mount, captured during the Revolutionary War. The horse was five feet four inches high at the top of the shoulders (sixteen hands), a gigantic creature in comparison with the colonial horse. He was offered for sale but evidently the price paid was not remarkable, for there is no record of it or of who got him. Whoever the man was who bought the colonel's horse, he was the first New Englander to own a Thoroughbred, a horse that would later become valuable throughout the New World.

The little horse of old colonial days maintained his popularity for some time after the Revolution. But the variety

of jobs he had to do was increasing and some of those jobs demanded qualities he did not always have.

Justin Morgan Founds a Breed

In early colonial days, the job of the horse had been to carry a rider safely, quickly, and easily over rough trails or through the woods. But by 1780, many horses, especially in the cities, wore harness and pulled wheeled vehicles. Some of the vehicles were buggies in which doctors, merchants, and other busy people rode in their daily work. Others were wagons belonging to butchers, bakers, or other tradespeople. Some very large wagons transported heavy freight.

On the farms, horses were replacing oxen as work animals and wore heavy harness. Whenever they could, farmers who raised horses sought out stallions whose colts would put power into the collar to do all kinds of work.

In 1789 such a stallion was foaled by a little mare of
the old colonial type. She was not owned by a farmer. A
schoolteacher in Springfield, Massachusetts, owned her and
had mated her with a stallion who was a son of a Thoroughbred imported from England. The colt, grandson of a horse
of the new English breed and son of a mare of old American
stock, was destined to become the sire of a new breed of
horse perfect for all the new jobs horses had to do in early
nineteenth-century America. Nobody paid much attention
to the teacher's colt, who was named Figure. He grew up
and learned to work in harness. His teacher-owner moved to
Randolph, Vermont. That teacher, like most men in his
profession, was frequently in need of money. For fifteen
dollars he rented his young horse to a Robert Evans, who
had contracted a job of clearing fifteen acres of land for a

Mr. Fish. The trees growing on the land were large; but when felled and cut into logs, none was too large for the teacher's horse to drag to the nearby sawmill.

At the end of one day's work on his contract, Evans, seated sidewise on his rented horse, was riding home, one hand on the hames and one heel hanging against a trace chain. As he passed the local tavern, he was hailed by a friend. He tied Figure to the hitch rail and went into the tavern to join his friends. They were all excited about a pulling match, a common sport in those days. There was a log, they told Evans, about two hundred feet from the logway at the mill. The team that had dragged it there had not been able to get it any farther. Several of the men at the tavern had horses of which they were very proud. Each of them was betting that his horse could move the log.

Evans walked back to the mill and took a look at the log. When he returned he said, "I'll wager a gallon of rum that my horse can put that log in the logway in three pulls."

Cheering, the little crowd followed Evans and Figure to the mill. Taking a singletree from the doubletree abandoned by the team that could move the log no farther, Evans fastened it to the log chain and hooked Figure's traces to it. Then he stood back and surveyed the log.

"That's a mighty small log to move for a gallon of rum," he said. "Why don't two or three of you men jump on it?"

Three men piled onto the log. Evans gathered up the reins. The 950-pound horse gently began to mouth the bit.

Evans spoke quietly to him. Figure settled into the collar
and dug in his feet. The great muscles of his loins and
haunches bunched up and began to ripple. The chain ground
tight on the log, and the log began to move. At an ever
increasing speed it moved until it had covered half the distance to the logway and the three riders, spattered by **dirt**
thrown up by Figure's digging hoofs had tumbled off.

A quiet "Whoa" from Evans stopped the little horse
for a breathing spell. In two more pulls Figure landed the
log in the logway.

From that day, the fame of the teacher's horse began to
spread. Farmers around Randolph brought their mares to
Figure to get colts that were strong. Parade marshals asked
for him to lead parades on the Fourth of July and other
days of celebration. With bands playing behind him, Figure
stepped so proudly that everybody cheered him. Today,
our parade horses wear special heavy shoes and have very
long toes so that they have to pick up their feet very high.
Without special shoes or long toes, Figure's feet snapped
up like steel springs. His full-crested neck was proudly
arched. His big wide-apart eyes took in everything. From
his delicately curved, alert ears, with their tips so close
together, to his sensitive muzzle, his head was more beautiful than any ever before seen in Vermont.

"Sure, he's a pretty horse, and he can pull when he
wears harness," said a jealous onlooker while Figure was
prancing past him at the head of a Fourth of July parade.

"Yep, he may be a pretty prancer and a work horse, but I have a horse that can outwalk him or outtrot him, any day under saddle!"

And so other contests were planned for Figure and other wagers were won by his backers. In 1796, two horses, Sweepstakes and Silvertail, were brought all the way from New York to race him. They were the winners of many running races, which means races at the gallop. Figure beat both of them easily. His master must have felt sorry for the owner of Silvertail, because he offered him two chances to win back his money. He said he would put up the money

as prize for a walking race or trotting race, whichever Silver-tail's owner wanted, but the offer was refused.

Today, such a remarkable horse would bring a high price if sold. He would be kept in a fine stable with the best care; but in 1800, only Thoroughbreds imported from England were fashionable with the wealthy. Figure was sold again and again for a modest price, and always to a man who needed a horse for work, though he might run him in a matched race now and then. Four times the little horse was taken as part payment of a debt.

His original name, Figure, was forgotten. It was not a very catchy name for a horse, anyway. Perhaps Justin Morgan, the teacher who raised him, had chosen the name because a schoolmaster in 1800 was supposed to teach children to read, write, and figure. We, of course, say he taught reading, writing, and arithmetic. Whatever Justin Morgan's reason was for calling his colt Figure, the name did not last. As word about this horse, who could do so many things, spread among men who used horses to earn a living, he became known as "that Morgan horse." Finally, he was referred to as Justin Morgan, the name we know him by today.

Though he changed hands many times, the stout little horse always worked for his owners. And he continued to win fame by defeating all challengers in running, walking, trotting, and pulling contests until one evening, at the end of a hard day in work harness pulling a wagon, he was turned into a lot with other horses and was kicked. The night was cold and snow started to fall. There was no shelter and no one to care for the wound in his side. Inflammation set in and he died. He was thirty-two years old.

Though the great little horse Justin Morgan died in 1821, his fame continued to grow through his sons and daughters. One of the most unusual qualities of "the big little horse" was his ability to pass on to his sons and daughters his strength, speed, and beauty. Two of the six most famous sons of Justin Morgan were known only by the names of the men who raised them—the Hawkins horse and the Fenton horse. They were foaled in 1806 and 1808, respectively. Two others of the famous six were known by the names of their sires and the names of the men who raised them. They were Sherman Morgan, foaled in 1808, and Woodbury Morgan, foaled in 1816. Another of the six, foaled in 1812, was called Bullrush Morgan. Perhaps he, like Moses in the Bible, was found in the bulrushes. Only one of the six had a name not connected with an owner or sire. He was called Revenue, foaled in 1815.

These six sons of Justin Morgan were not only famous in their own day, but through their descendants they are represented in the most fashionable breeds of American horses today—the American Saddle Horse, the Quarter Horse, the Standardbred, and the Tennessee Walking Horse. Of all important breeds today, only the Arabian and the Thoroughbred owe no debt for their success to Justin Morgan.

Racing and the Standardbred

Justin Morgan had to earn his oats and hay by spending most of his life wearing a collar and harness with chain traces for pulling heavy loads. He was given no more care than any ordinary work horse. The lives of his famous sons were different. Fast trotting horses were becoming fashionable. No longer was the imported Thoroughbred the only horse favored by the rich and stylish city folks. Then too, the Revolutionary War had taught Americans the importance of good roads. And with roads came new wheeled vehicles. More and more, the rich and fashionable rode on wheels, and trotting horses were much better than any others to pull them.

In 1825 a group of fashionable New Yorkers organized the New York Trotting Club. In 1826 they built a race track and called it the Centreville Course. It was located near an important road, the Jamaica Turnpike. Three years later, a group of fashionable Philadelphians organized a club to promote trotting races. They called it the Philadelphia Hunting Park Association. Until this time all organized races had been run under saddle. But many trotting-horse owners wanted to race their horses in harness, hitched to carts. The Philadelphia club finally wrote into their rules that trotting matches in harness could be held if a majority of the club's members voted for them.

The growing popularity of trotting races gave Justin Morgan's sons and daughters and granddaughters and their offspring the chance they needed to become famous in the big cities of America. Sherman Morgan, one of the famous six sons, sired a colt by a mare called Old Narragansett, a Narragansett Pacer. The colt was called Black Hawk. He was a champion trotter but his greatest fame came from his son, Ethan Allen. No horse could beat Ethan Allen at the trot under saddle. Then he was challenged to races in harness. No single horse could beat him. Finally, he was challenged to race in a team—two horses pulling a vehicle. No trotter could be found that was fast enough to keep up with him, so one of the fastest running horses of the day was hitched beside him.

The matched race agreed upon was five one-mile heats. That means that the horses were to have five contests, each one mile in length, with sufficient time in between to rest and cool off.

On the Fashion Course race track on Long Island on June 21, 1867, Ethan Allen not only won, with a mate galloping at his side, but he won over the fastest horse of his day, Dexter, who was not hampered by a mate. More than that, Ethan Allen broke all trotting records of the day by trotting the three winning heats in two minutes and fifteen seconds, two minutes and sixteen seconds, and two minutes and nineteen seconds.

In the year of this historic race, carriage makers had become as common and as busy as automobile makers today. Cities were growing and business and professional men wanted faster transportation. The carriage makers were designing lighter and faster buggies and faster horses were needed to pull them. Prices rose for fast-driving horses. Breeders of trotters were quick to respond by more careful selection and mating of their stock. In 1876 the best breeders organized into the National Association of Trotting Horse Breeders. This was the beginning of systematic horse breeding in America. The breeders adopted a "registry." This is the only means of keeping a breed pure. The name of a horse that meets the standards set by an association keeping a registry is recorded. Colts from registered parents can be recorded. In this way a breed is kept pure; horses inherit from their registered parents the qualities wanted in a particular breed.

The Association called their breed the Standardbred, because one of its rules stated that no horse should be registered unless he could trot a mile in two minutes and thirty seconds, which was called the standard of speed.

Tom Hal and His Offspring

While city people demanded and paid higher and higher prices for fast trotters to pull buggies on the streets and light carts on race tracks, the ever increasing farm and plantation land of America called for horses of a different kind. America was growing. Planters from Virginia and farmers from the north were pushing westward for more land. Virginians pushed into Tennessee and even into Kentucky. Farmers who had heard of the fertile land found by Daniel Boone and other pioneers in Kentucky had been quick to follow his trail.

Some of the early Virginia planters were aristocrats from England. They liked elegance and ease. So did their children and grandchildren. The early colonial horses for all their speed and endurance could hardly be called elegant. By 1800 elegant and fast English Thoroughbreds were being imported into Virginia, but they did not have the easy gaits demanded by men pushing into new country where the lack of roads still made horseback riding the only means of transportation. Then too, Thoroughbreds were too nervous to be used by the planters who had to ride a horse to oversee their plantations.

This demand for a horse having ease, elegance, and speed soon made famous some stallions of a new kind. They were usually related through their grandparents and great-grandparents to the old colonial horses, the Canadian Pacers, the Narragansetts, the Dutch, the Morgans, the Standardbreds, and English Thoroughbreds. Their fame rested on their possession of the qualities needed in the farmlands of Kentucky, Tennessee, and Missouri, and upon their ability to pass those qualities on to their colts, their "get."

One of the first of the new crop of famous stallions was owned by a town doctor. Towns, of course, did spring up in the new farming country, and doctors had to travel the rough roads and trails unsuitable for buggies.

A Doctor Boswell of Lexington, Kentucky, had many patients, both in town and far out in the country. His work was hard on horses. He had heard of a stallion in Philadelphia that was said to have such energy that he was never known to lie down except to roll. Even when tied, the stallion would keep moving as far as his halter would permit. When eating in his box stall, he would grab a mouthful of feed and walk about his stall until his food was chewed.

Doctor Boswell went to Philadelphia, bought the stallion, and rode him back to Lexington. He found the horse, Tom Hal, to be all that reports had indicated. Soon after buying

Tom, the doctor received an urgent call, delivered by messenger from Louisville. A patient of his who had moved to that city was seriously ill and thought only Doctor Boswell could save his life. Friends begged the busy doctor not to take time away from his home-town patients to travel all the way, over eighty miles, to Louisville.

"Why," said one of them, "it will take you four or five days to make the trip and the hard riding will exhaust you so that you will not be able to practice for another day or two."

"I have one hundred dollars," said the doctor, "that says Tom will take me there and back in two days without tiring me more than a rocking chair would in the same length of time."

The friend took the bet and lost. Tom Hal "paced," as the easy gait was then called, all the way; and Doctor Boswell tended his patients as usual on his return.

In addition to his fame for speed, endurance, and ease, Tom Hal also became known as the most sure-footed of stallions. Once, when this quality of Tom's was questioned, Doctor Boswell ordered ten rails to be placed on the ground. He bet the questioner ten dollars that Tom could pace over the rails without touching any of them. The doctor never lost a bet on Tom Hal.

The best horse breeders of Kentucky brought their mares to mate with the famous stallion. Before his death in 1843 at the age of 41, Tom's foals and their foals had become famous. There is no record of Tom Hal's breeding. He

was imported to Philadelphia from Canada and, like many Canadian Pacers, was said to be a mixture of old colonial and Dutch breeding. A daughter of Tom Hal was mated with a great-great-grandson of Sherman Morgan. The result of this mating was a horse called Cabell's Lexington. In 1879 when he was sixteen years old, and a comparatively young horse, he died from a kick by a mare. At that time it was said that he was the sire of over half of the most famous horses in Kentucky and Tennessee.

War Horses and Show Horses

By the outbreak of the Civil War, horse shows were becoming popular. They were usually a part of a county fair, but sometimes on court day in county seats, a horse show was held independently. The most popular class of any show was the one for five-gaited horses. However, the war soon put an end to horse shows. All the best horses of Kentucky and Tennessee were mustered into service, regardless of age. Gaines's Denmark, today considered the most important ancestor of the American Saddle Horse, was only one of many almost equally important. He was ten years old, but he served his years as an officer's charger in active service and returned home to sire great offspring.

The record southern saddlers achieved as cavalry horses has never been equaled. These were the horses later to be recorded in the registries of two breeds—the American Saddle Horse and the Tennesse Walking Horse. A report of the United States government, called the *Nineteenth Annual Report of the Bureau of Animal Industry*, says that these horses "stood the terrible strain where other breeds gave way under the test of great marches."

In twenty-five hours, in August of 1862, a troop of southern cavalry rode ninety miles *to begin* a surprise attack on a garrison. There was no resting from the ninety-mile march before the attack was launched.

In 1863, General John Hunt Morgan, starting with 2,460 men mounted on Tennessee and Kentucky saddlers, raided through Ohio and Indiana. They were ambushed, pursued, and confronted by Union forces of far greater numbers. Once they were turned back from an attempted crossing of the Ohio River by fire from two gunboats. For three weeks this cavalry command fought, burned bridges, swam rivers, foraged for supplies, and averaged over twenty miles a day. After those three weeks, what was left of the command averaged over thirty-five miles a day for six days while fighting off pursuers from all sides.

Twice during the raid, when their horses were badly in need of rest and food, the Confederate soldiers took the best horses they could find from breeding farms in Ohio and Indiana but none of these horses lasted more than a day in the company of the Confederate horses.

When General Lee's surrender ended the war, General Grant allowed the Confederate soldiers to take home their horses. Some of these soldiers found no other livestock left on their farms when they got home. The horses that had carried them through the war had to help them plow their fields and plant their cotton and corn.

The Kentucky and Tennessee saddlers were used for all kinds of jobs. When horse shows again were flourishing, dealers and trainers paid good prices for the best of them. Because they had learned to do all kinds of work and, when well fed and cared for, were the most elegant of horses, they were used as fine carriage horses in the cities. In 1888 a colt was foaled on the farm of S. S. Thompson in Fleming County, Kentucky. He was named Glorious Red Cloud. When he grew up, he was bought by Thomas W. Lawson of Boston, Massachusetts, for what was then a record price—ten thousand dollars. Mr. Lawson wanted him for a harness horse. He was such a fancy harness horse that Mr. Lawson entered him in the Madison Square Garden Horse Show in New York City in 1899. At that show, Glorious Red Cloud won the Waldorf-Astoria Challenge Cup as the best horse of his kind in the show. His brothers and sisters were also famous, winning many championships as gaited saddle horses and as harness horses. Lord Brilliant, a brother, won the Waldorf-Astoria Cup three times—in 1900, 1901, and 1902.

In 1903 an American judge, William Moore, wanted to own the finest harness horse in America. He went to England where a special breed of horse, the Hackney, had been developed specifically as a harness horse. Judge Moore paid twelve thousand dollars for Forest King, the finest Hackney he could find. He brought him back and entered him in the Madison Square Garden Horse Show, hoping to win the championship. But Lord Brilliant defeated the Hackney, winning the Heavy-Harness Championship.

American Saddle Horses

These horses of Kentucky and Tennessee had no competitors as saddle horses and could beat even the best imported horses in harness. They continued to increase in price. Breeders had organized in 1891 and set up a registry. At that time they called themselves the National Saddle Horse Breeders' Association. In 1899 they voted to change the name to The American Saddle Horse Breeders Association. They decided upon a list of seventeen of the most famous stallions of the day, each of whom was producing foals of the type most highly prized as Saddle Horses. To get into the registry, a colt had to prove that he was closely related to one or more of the seventeen stallions.

In 1902 the Association met and solved the problem of defining and naming the gaits of the Saddle Horse. Horsemen called the different gaits performed by the saddler by the name that was used in his locality. Some still called any gait other than a trot and between a walk and a gallop a pace. Some called the fast four-beat gait, just faster than a walk, a rack; still others called it a running walk. There was a difference of opinion about how many gaits a Saddle Horse should be able to perform. Some horsemen stoutly demanded that the saddler must be able to do a fast, true pace; others just as stoutly declared that any horse that did a true pace—in which the two feet on the same side struck the ground at the same time—was not a Saddle Horse and should be kept in harness on a race track.

The Association gave these problems much study and decided that the American Saddle Horse should be either three-gaited or five-gaited. The three-gaited horse should walk, trot, and canter. The five-gaited horse should have these three gaits and two others. One of the two additional gaits would be called the rack (formerly called a single-foot

by some horsemen). It must be a true four-beat gait with exactly the same fraction of time between each two hoof-beats and it must be performed at least as fast as the rate of a mile in three minutes. The other additional gait of the five-gaited horse would be called a slow gait. This slow gait could be any one of several easy gaits just faster than a walk; that is, about the rate of from four to seven miles an hour. The various gaits permitted to be used as a slow gait were the running walk, a true four-beat gait; the slow pace, a pace of broken rhythm in which the hind foot of each side strikes the ground just before the forefoot on the same side does; or a fox trot, a slow trot with broken rhythm in which the forefoot strikes the ground just before the hind foot of the opposite side strikes. These are the gaits of the Saddle Horse to this day, though he is now required to do them with an artificially high action and does the trot and rack at such speed that they almost seem like different gaits from those of the early saddlers.

In the 1902 meeting, the Association took another important action; they shortened the list of seventeen foundation sires. The names that were removed were put into the main part of the register. Then in 1908, all of the horses but one, Denmark, were put into the main part of the register, and Denmark was proclaimed the foundation sire. This may seem confusing because all the colts related to Denmark that were of the Saddle Horse type, and there were many of them, were related to him through his son, Gaines's Denmark. It is probably to Gaines's Denmark's mother that they owed most of the qualities admired in colts related to Denmark. She was a Cockspur mare. The Cockspurs were a strain of the old colonial saddlers with some Narragansett and some Canadian Pacer blood in them. Probably the things the Saddle Horse inherited from Denmark were increase of size and length of neck. Denmark was a son of an English Thoroughbred. His mother was a granddaughter of English Thoroughbreds. Denmark was a four-mile race horse, but was more elegant in build and movement than most race horses. Neither he nor any of his foals, except those descended from him through Gaines's Denmark, could do the saddle gaits. It is perhaps his good fortune in having one great son that entitles him to his place as foundation sire. There is not a good American Saddle Horse today that does not have the name of that son, Gaines's Denmark, on his pedigree.

The Rise of Horse Shows

For a quarter of a century the American Saddle Horse reigned supreme as the horse for use under saddle and in fancy harness, though other breeds dominated the race track and the utility-buggy-horse trade. Whenever a man of means wanted a fine carriage pair or a horse to drive singly in an elegant vehicle, he looked for an American Saddle Horse. In horse shows, except in parts of the country that carefully and closely followed the style of England, the leading event was the five-gaited stake for Saddle Horses. In Chicago, St. Louis, and Louisville large sums of money were put up for the stake. Ten thousand dollars was put up in Louisville. Soon the big cities of the West Coast were also holding big stakes. Saddle Horses that could win stakes were commanding high prices.

Of course not all American Saddle Horses could be stake winners. Most of them were raised and sold as fine mounts for people who could afford the best. The great stakes were tests of a horse's ability to be a fine mount for his owner at the five gaits. Some of the contests lasted for over two hours. A horse that could, for the greater part of that time, do a fast rack and trot proved his ability to be a mount for any owner to ride with pride.

The Automobile and the Big Shows

About 1910 something happened to put an end to the glory of the American Saddle Horse: the automobile captured the favor of Americans and won it away from the horse. Men of means no longer spent their money for a fine horse to ride or drive; they bought a motorcar. For almost twenty years there was little market for fine riding or driving horses. Prices for Saddle Horses that could win prizes in shows remained high, but breeders could not run their farms on the money they got from the few horses that could win prizes in horse shows. Many of them therefore had to stop raising horses.

Though many horse breeders quit raising horses, horse shows continued to attract crowds. They became more popular, and great buildings were built for them—the Cow Palace in San Francisco, for example. (It was called Cow Palace because it was used for showing cattle in addition to showing horses, and the West is known as cattle country.) Madison Square Garden in New York was relocated and rebuilt to hold bigger horse shows than before. Saddle Horses that could win in shows increased in price. In 1926, Edna May's King, a descendant of Justin Morgan, the Cockspurs, and the colonial horses, was sold by Revel English, one of the greatest showmen of the day, to a man in Spofford, Texas, for forty thousand dollars. Other show horses soon were commanding similar prices.

Edna May's King had a quality that came into fashion with the increase of horse shows all over America. The new quality demanded was bigness. Many of the winning horses of Edna May's King's day were also grandchildren or great-grandchildren of Edna May's King's grandfather, Harrison

Chief, who added great size to the American Saddle Horse breed. He weighed 1300 pounds which is one third more than most of the best horses originally registered in the American Saddle Horse registry.

Size became important because the American Saddle Horse had become something to show rather than to ride. Of course, here and there, Saddle Horses were kept for riding or driving by their owners, but the big prices went for the show horses, and breeders were selecting mares and stallions that would produce colts that might grow into show horses. In the show ring, a big horse is much more impressive than a little horse. He catches the eye of the audience and the judges.

In addition to size, other qualities were needed in a horse intended purely for show. He had to pick his feet up higher than any horse could step naturally. He had to hold his tail in an artificial way. His neck and shoulders had to present an imposing appearance. To get horses to raise their feet high, trainers let the feet grow long and used heavy shoes on their horses. A horse's feet (hoofs) grow, like a human's fingernails and toenails. When horses go without shoes and are on dry ground, they keep their feet worn down so that most of them have feet that are from three to four and a half inches long at the front of the hoof. If a horse is used much under saddle or in harness, he must be shod. The shoes prevent the wearing down of the feet, so the horseshoer, also called a farrier or blacksmith, pares down the growth with a tool called a hoof nipper (sometimes referred to as a pair of hoof nippers) each time he renews the shoes. If he did not do so, the feet would get so long that they would put a great strain on the legs of the horse, for the hoof is sloping and as it grows it gets farther forward than it should to be directly under the leg and bear the weight properly. Another reason the smithy pares the foot is to keep the outer wall of the hoof short enough to allow the V-shaped pad at the rear of the bottom of a horse's foot, called the frog, to bear part of the weight. This is necessary to keep the circulation of the foot operating properly and to keep the rear of the hoof from contracting and pinching the live, inner part of the foot, much as an ingrown toenail pinches a human toe.

When the American Saddle Horse became valuable as a show-ring spectacle, each trainer tried to get his horses to make a more spectacular show than the others. He wanted his horses to pick their feet up higher than all others. To do so, he had the smithy stop paring their feet down because long hoofs (often more than five inches in length) made them pick their feet up higher. He also put heavy shoes on them for the same reason. With such feet and shoes, horses could not perform at high speeds for an hour or two, as they had done in shows in an earlier time. Horse-show classes were shortened, therefore, until some of them lasted only fifteen or twenty minutes. Even the big stakes lasted little over half an hour.

To get horses to hold their tails in a more spectacular manner, the owners had operations performed on them. To make the horses' necks and shoulders look more imposing, showmen devised a way of putting a saddle farther toward the rear than a saddle normally stays on a horse's back. This made the shoulders look more imposing. Up to this time, riding saddles (not racing saddles) had been made to fit a horse's back so that the front of the saddle stayed just behind the shoulder blades. The skirts of most saddles, the part under the knees and upper calves of the rider, usually curved forward. The new show saddles were made so that their fronts stayed several inches behind the shoulder blades, and some were equipped with rubberized girths to keep the girths from slipping forward and allowing the saddle to get out of place. The skirts no longer curved forward.

To please the audience and the judges, a show horse had to look spirited. Trainers not only cultivated the natural liveliness of their horses but used methods of training that increased the horse's natural nervousness. The result was that a show horse could be ridden only by a professional trainer or someone taught by a professional.

The American Saddle Horse again had his place in the sun; he had no competitors in his field—the show ring. His reign, however, was soon to be challenged.

America Rides Again

Grownups in America were finding that horseback riding was a very healthful and enjoyable recreation. Younger Americans were finding that a horse is fun to ride and that he is a delightful pet. Many people living where city ordinances forbade them to keep horses moved to the suburbs where they could keep a horse or two. Men of means who could afford it bought good American Saddle Horses to ride for their own pleasure. But when they got the horses home, they found that the professionally trained horses were too nervous to be ridden with safety or pleasure. Others found that the feet of the American Saddle Horses they bought had been made unsuitable for use on anything but an especially prepared ring. Some found that the loins of their horses had been injured by show saddles and others objected to the tails that had been operated **upon.**

The Tennessee Walker

Aware of the difficulty of finding fine, easy-gaited horses
that could be ridden with pleasure outside the show ring,
a horseman in Tennessee had an idea. He knew that in
the back country of Tennessee there were good easy-gaited
horses of unspoiled disposition. These horses were not as
speedy or as handsome as the gaited show horses, but they
were beautiful nonetheless and their easy gaits made them
a delight to ride. So Mr. Burt Hunter and some of his friends
had a meeting in Lewisburg, Tennessee, on April 27, 1935,
to discuss how they could bring their horses to the attention
of men who wanted to buy fine horses that could be easily
ridden by their owners.

The men who met at Lewisburg had been raising their
horses for years for a small market in the southern states.
Plantation owners bought them because of the horses' easy

gaits and pleasant dispositions. An overseer could be in the saddle all day directing the work on his plantation without becoming fatigued or irritated with his horse.

People had been calling these horses Plantation Horses.

But when the breeders met at Lewisburg, they decided on the name Tennessee Walking Horse. They formed themselves into an association and called it the Tennessee Walking Horse Breeders' Association of America. They selected the name Walking Horse because their horses could do a running walk unlike that of any other horse. It was smoother than the running walk of any five-gaited show horse and was done with a long, easy swinging stride. The Tennessee horses could do that walk for hours without tiring themselves or their riders.

On that April day in Lewisburg, the Association made up a list of the finest horses in Tennessee to be named foundation sires in the registry. At the head of the list was a horse called Allan. They wrote him down as Allan F-1 because he was foundation horse number one.

Allan was a beautiful black stallion, five feet (fifteen hands) high at the top of his shoulders. He had a long graceful neck, short strong back, and long powerful hips, on which the tail was set high and carried proudly. One of his great-grandfathers was a grandson of Justin Morgan. Another was descended from famous winners of trotting races on the tracks of America. The easy movement of the Walker was also inherited from other great-grandparents who were members of the old families of easy-gaited saddlers—the Tom Hals, Cockspurs, and others.

To get the attention of the buying public for their newly named breed, the Association advertised in magazines and on the radio. They produced a motion picture of Tennessee

Walking Horses. But most important of all, they gave the officers of their association power to control the sale of registered horses so that nobody who bought one would get a poor specimen. They also wrote down rigid rules about the gaits that a Walker must perform and the way he must be shown in the ring.

The gaits of their horse, they decided, must be the walk, the running walk, and the canter. The walk must be a four-beat gait with no tendency toward a pace. The running walk must be at the rate of from six to eight miles an hour and done without lifting the feet so high that the horse wastes energy. The canter must be slow; slow enough so that the horse can easily glide into it from his running walk. It must be done gracefully, with a beautiful rocking motion. They also ruled that no Tennessee Walking Horse could be shown with excessively long feet or weighted shoes.

In a very few years the Tennessee Walking Horse became popular as a fine pleasure horse. Because of their fame, horse shows from New York to California began to include classes for Walking Horses in their programs. The Association kept a careful eye on all showings of Walkers and saw to it that the gaits were those the Association had originally described in the rule book. It was not until after the death of Burt Hunter, the man who first had the idea of bringing the Walking Horse to public attention, that the Walker joined the Saddlebred as a high-priced, show-ring attraction. Today, the Walker performs a gait called a running walk at more than twice the speed of the running walk of the old

Plantation Horse. His feet are now so long and his shoes so weighted that steel bands over the hoofs, in addition to nails, are needed to keep the shoes from flying off.

The Tennessee Walking Horse was the last of the great breeds to be developed in North America and organized into a registry east of the Mississippi River. The Morgan, the Standardbred, the American Saddle Horse, and the Tennessee Walker all came from the eastern half of America. The next breed to have a registry came to fame in the West.

The Quarter Horse

While the descendants of colonial horses were being selected and organized into breeds and developed into fancy show horses and race horses, the descendants of the first horses brought to this continent were running wild or growing up on the great ranges of the West with little attention to blood lines on any but a few ranches. Those few ranches that did any systematic breeding raised horses because they needed horses in the business of raising cattle. The horses running wild had so deteriorated since the days when the conquistadors brought their ancestors from Spain that they were, with few exceptions, unfit for working cattle.

"Our business is raising beef. We would buy horses for work if we could, but the kind that will stand up under our work aren't available; so we have to raise them," said the manager of a ranch in Arizona that for many miles straddled the international border between Mexico and Arizona. On that ranch good stallions were selected or imported from the East. Each stallion would be turned on the range with twenty native mares of the old Spanish stock. The stallion and his mares would each be branded with the same special brand called a herd brand, in addition to the ranch brand. Those stallions whose offspring were not of the desired kind were replaced. The best of the offspring was saved for breeding.

A few of the great ranches of Texas were equally systematic in their horse raising. Some of them were so successful in producing horses of quality that polo players from the East began looking to Texas for good mounts. For a few years prices for polo mounts were so good that some ranchers in Texas started to raise horses for the polo market. This business, however, did not last long, for the rules of polo were changed. Originally, the rules would not allow the use of ponies higher than fifty-eight inches ($14\frac{1}{4}$ hands). But that limitation of height was taken out of the rules and the game was changed in other ways so that polo players began to use race horses, Thoroughbreds, with which the little Texas ponies could not compete.

For working cattle, however, the little western horses had no equal. Some of them did not weigh over eight hundred pounds. Few were over fifty-eight inches tall. Few had pretty heads; usually their eyes were set higher than those of some of the better bred horses of the East. They did not look particularly stout, but their looks were deceiving. With more than two hundred pounds on their backs they could work from dawn until the shadows grew long in the afternoon.

The story of a little mouse-colored horse called Musawg shows the kind of work they did. Musawg got his name because of his color and because he was a little more compactly built than most of the horses wearing the 88 brand. Both his build and his color suggested the musk hog, sometimes called a javelina, that ran wild in the Superstition Mountains of Arizona, on which the 88 Ranch was located.

One of the roughest places Musawg worked was Haunted Canyon, a little pocket high in the mountains containing good springs, edible grass, and mesquite. Cattle could live and grow in that little canyon from one year's end to the next without care from human hands. They saw humans only at branding time and on those rare occasions when medical care was given to them. Consequently, they were a bit on the wild side and hard to handle. A wrong move by a mounted man, or any move at the wrong time, would frighten them and they would scatter like quail, giving the cowboys hours of work to bunch them again.

Musawg's rider, Jake Dawkins, a seasoned cowhand, rode with a slack rein. The little gelding knew when to freeze like a rock and give a cow time to quiet down, and when to dart out in front of a cow to keep her from dodging back into the brush. Often Musawg would make a dash over boulders that another rider would not dare lead a quiet horse over on a walk.

One midafternoon, Musawg's rider and four other cowboys had gathered a small herd of cattle and started them down the mountain for the corrals. Suddenly a rider in the rear yelled, "Look out, Jake!"

Just behind Jake, who was riding about midway on one side of the little herd, a big roan steer had snorted, twisted his tail in the air, and shot off at right angles from the herd. They were on a ridge between two canyons; and the steer headed down the side of the ridge, which was covered with thorny cactus, boulders, and slide rock. He was making a beeline for the bottom of the canyon in which the mesquite grew so thick that he could easily lose any pursuer and head back up the mountain for Haunted Canyon.

Musawg spun on his haunches and shot down the mountainside, his feet sending rocks bounding ahead of him toward the canyon below. Jake took down his rope. The steer had almost gained the shelter of the mesquite when a loop of rope settled over his horns. Though they were still going slightly downgrade and the steer was below him, Musawg sat back on his haunches and dug his feet in among the rocks to take the shock of the rope when the steer hit the end of it. The jerk of the rope pulled the little horse to his knees and sent the steer into a complete somersault. Before the runaway could regain his wind, Musawg was between him and the mesquite brush, ready to outdodge him and send him back up the ridge.

Of course the men who spent so much of their lives in the saddle did not confine their use of horses to work. Rodeos and races were their amusements. There were also Sunday afternoon roping contests and once in a while a contest between cutting horses. A cutting horse is one that can go quietly into a herd of cattle without exciting it, bring out an animal his rider wants to separate from the herd, and put it wherever it is supposed to go, no matter how hard it tries to get back to the herd. Some cattle are so frantic to get back to the herd that they jump and dodge back and forth faster than a rider can direct a horse, so the horse has to work on his own as soon as his rider shows him which animal he wants out of the herd. A good cutting horse learns to anticipate the movements of a cow so that at each dodge she makes to get back to the herd, she finds the horse has dodged a split second before her and blocks her return to the herd. Cutting horses move so fast that even the best of riders have to hold on to the saddle horn to keep their seats. Some cutting horses were so gifted that their riders would show off the skill of their mounts by taking the bridle off so onlookers could see that the horse was doing the work entirely on his own.

Stallions of most of the eastern breeds were to be found on the big ranches serving as herd sires to improve the riding stock. Whenever the offspring of these stallions would prove to be a good animal, his colts were sought after as breeding stock or as rodeo or race horses. Since there was no registry in the West, no record was kept of the blood.

But certain good stallions became well known because their descendants resembled them and were uniformly good race horses, rodeo mounts, or cow horses. Such descendants were known by the name of the head of their family, just as the descendants of Justin Morgan were known as Morgans. The favorite family of the early part of this century was the Steeldust. Mystery still surrounds the original Steeldust. Men who claimed to know what he was and where he came from were each talking about a different Steeldust. But the Steeldusts were so distinctive and so similar in appearance that there must have been one very great stallion that founded the family.

Almost as popular as the Steeldusts were the Copperbottoms. The head of that family was a Canadian horse brought to Kentucky in 1812. An old book has this description of Copperbottom: "Old Copperbottom was a bay roan, 15.2 hands high (62 inches), fine style, compact as a pony and had all the gaits; a good trotter, fast pacer; fox trot and running walk, and he stamped himself in all his colts."

Whether Old Copperbottom or one of his sons went west to found the family known by his name is not known, but even today most of the horses that carry his blood have his distinctive color and the "fine style" and the compactness of their ancestor.

Other great stallions that founded families in the west, though they themselves were of unknown breeding, were Sykes Rondo, Old Billy, Shilo, Traveler, and Peter McCue.

There was much argument about the breeding of each of these stallions after his descendants became popular. Some men were certain about the breeding of a particular horse but others were equally certain of facts contradicting them. One of the most illustrious stallions of the Traveler family had grandsons that won many of the quarter-mile races of their day (1940–1950). The stallion's very name King added to the confusion because there were several other well-known horses of that name. King's sire was a famous Mexican race horse called Zantanon. His mother's sire was Traveler, but she, too, carried Spanish blood.

Peter McCue was also made famous by a grandson, but not on the race track. That grandson, Old Sorrel, happened to be foaled on the King Ranch of Texas. Of the hundreds of horses raised on that ranch, Old Sorrel proved to be the best sire. Though he lost his eyesight he was kept as top sire and continued to produce the best colts on that vast spread. The manager of the King Ranch wanted to fix permanently the type of Old Sorrel in the horses of his ranch so he issued an order that was contrary to one of the most firmly held ideas of horse raisers all over the country —the idea that a horse bred to his own descendant will produce a deformed colt. Old Sorrel was mated with his own daughters and then to his granddaughters. Almost without exception the foals from these matings turned out to be the best ones on the ranch, though the foals of the granddaughters were considered a little better than their dams. They were, of course, excellent cow ponies, but a few of them got to the race track, others to horse shows and rodeos. It was the outstanding performance of these horses in public contests that spread the fame of the get of Old Sorrel.

By 1939, horse shows, rodeos, and race tracks had become big business throughout the Southwest. The most popular horses were the Steeldusts, the King Ranch horses, and the other families from the famous old sires. Of course, horsemen disagreed on which blood was best, but they all agreed on one thing—some sort of registry for western horses should be established so records of breeding could be kept. At the Fat Stock Show in Fort Worth, Texas, in 1939, the most prominent horsemen from all over the Southwest gathered together and decided on a name for a registry, The American Quarter Horse. They chose that name because they felt that their little horses were best known to the public as the fastest in the world in quarter-mile races. They planned a formal meeting to set up the registry the next year and on March 15, 1940, the American Quarter Horse Register was born.

As you might guess, this association of so many different kinds of horsemen had many arguments. Rules about the requirements a horse must satisfy in order to get his name written in the register were changed again and again. The first rules required that each horse registered must be inspected by an official inspector who decided whether or not the animal was of an acceptable type. The rules specified that three types of animals would be acceptable. Type A was what was known as the bulldog type. He was a chunky, thick, short-legged animal, very stout and hardy and capable of quick starts, stops, and turns (such performance is called being handy). Type B was less chunky and could look a little more like a Thoroughbred or a greyhound. He should show a little more speed than type A and he did not have to be quite as handy. Type C looked very much like a Thoroughbred, not as long-legged as some Thoroughbreds and not possessed of such high or sharp withers (the high part of a horse's backbone, which is just in front of the saddle) as some Thoroughbreds. As the registry grew, rules changed gradually. Less variety of type was permitted and more speed proved on race tracks was required. Finally, the registry was "closed," which means that only animals from a registered sire and dam could be accepted. That is the requirement today.

The range on which Musawg roped the wild roan steer was once the home of thousands of cattle. Today the United States government has wisely limited the number of cattle allowed on that range to less than 150. Each year cattle ranching is becoming more mechanized and fewer horses are needed. But Quarter Horse racing has become a big business involving many millions of dollars and thousands of horses yearly. The skills of men and horses, once so important on the open range, are now a part of one of the most popular entertainments in the country—rodeos. A good rodeo rope horse will bring many thousands of dollars if sold. Cutting contests are held in almost every city and

town in the West and are beginning to become popular in some places in the East. A cutting-horse enthusiast will pay many thousands of dollars for the perfect cutting horse. On the trail rides now popular from Vermont to California, the Quarter Horse is a favorite. Trail rides are groups of riders, from twenty-five to two hundred or more, who plan and go on all-day, overnight, or three- or four-day rides. Sometimes they carry meals and bed rolls on pack animals. Other times they arrange meal stops or overnight stops to be where trucks can carry the food, bedding, and horse feed. On one California trail ride in 1965 more than sixty Quarter Horses were present.

Breeds of Color

Until a few years ago, horses of striking color were not looked upon with favor by some lovers of fine animals. Solid bays, browns, sorrels, chestnuts (today all sorrels are called chestnut), blacks, grays, and whites with black skins were acceptable in all breeds. Duns and roans were usually acceptable. A bay horse's body, neck, and head are the color of red brick. Like some red bricks, some bay horses are lighter in color than others and some are darker. A bay horse's mane and tail are always black. His legs may be much darker than his body, even black, or one or more may be white. A brown horse also has a black mane and tail. His body and neck are brown like well-done toast. The term "sorrel" was, until recently, used for a horse a little darker in color than an orange and possessed of a mane and tail similar (sometimes a little lighter or a little darker) to the body color. A chestnut today may be sorrel or he may be the color of a chestnut or raw liver. His mane and tail may be darker or very light. A dun horse is the color of new buckskin gloves. A roan's coat is made of light and dark hairs closely mixed. White markings on the face and legs were always all right if they were not too large. For example, white on one or more legs was considered quite good unless the white extended above the knee or hock. Spotted horses—Pintos, piebalds, or skewbalds—were considered gaudy by people of good taste. Horses of such color were appropriate for wild west shows or as a drum horse (the horse that carries a drum in a cavalry band). Appaloosas and Palominos were equally out of place.

A Master of Foxhounds, the highest authority in a hunt club, was asked what he thought of Palominos (horses with golden colored bodies and white manes and tails) as hunters. He replied, "A Palomino at a hunt would be as out of place as a foxhunter's red formal coat at a rodeo."

Today all this discrimination against color seems a little silly. Strikingly colored horses have venerable history, stretching back in time to the beginning of human records and probably beyond. North Africa seems to have been the home of most of the strikingly colored horses. Names of countries and national boundaries have changed repeatedly in North Africa, but at one time the countries of the coastal region of North Africa were called the Barbary States, so for centuries the horses coming from there have been called Barbs. There is probably not a well-known breed of horses today that does not carry some Barb blood. For centuries, Barbs were imported into many lands.

The Greeks, long before the birth of Christ, were introduced to the excellence of Barb horses by the Numidians. The Numidians seemingly loved to fight, for apparently they fought as hired cavalry for any nation that would pay them. One Greek historian tells of their horses and horsemanship. He says that horses of Numidian mercenaries were so responsive to their riders that they were ridden without bridles; the horsemen, carrying weapons in both hands, drove the enemy before them.

When Hannibal crossed the Alps to invade Italy, Numidian mercenaries in his army would dash out in disarray, riding like amateurs, some tumbling off their horses. When they had lured their pursuers some distance from the main army, the Numidians on their spotted horses would whirl about, a weapon in each hand, and wipe out the dupes of their ruse.

Not all Barb horses were strikingly colored, but in any group of them, some were bound to be spotted, speckled, or colored like Palominos. There was Barb blood in the horses of the conquistadors. That is why so many of the horses of South America and the southwestern United States are strikingly colored.

The first North Americans to admire the striking colors of the Spanish horses were the Nez Percé and Palouse Indians who lived in ideal horse-raising country in the region of the Palouse River of what is now western Idaho and eastern Washington. They selected, and carefully bred, horses whose colors have been called speckled, domino, calico, polka dot, leopard, pied, and similar names. The explorers Lewis and Clark wrote that the horses of the Nez Percé "are pied with large spots of white irregularly scattered and intermixed with black, brown, bay, or some other dark color." As their fame spread, these horses became known as the "Fantail Appalouse" all over the range land. The name came from the phrase, "a Palouse horse," because these horses were favorites of the Palouse Indians. White settlers and miners wanted the land of the Nez Percé Indians, of course. The white people shot the Indians, made and broke treaties with them, and finally drove them onto a reservation in Oregon. In 1877, their leader, Chief Joseph, led his people, with about three thousand horses, north. They made a 1600-mile flight during which they fought off pursuing white troops in thirteen battles, losing nine hundred braves in one battle. Chief Joseph had almost reached the Canadian border when he was forced to surrender. Only 1100 of the "Fantail Appalouse" horses survived until the surrender. After the surrender they were turned loose and the Nez Percé were sent to a reservation in Oklahoma.

The Palomino

Another tribe of Indians who bred horses of striking color, especially the Palomino, was the Comanche. Color was not the only virtue of these horses, as a troop of cavalry of the Texas frontier learned the hard way. Officers of that troop were amused by the unusual color of the Indian horses. As the soldiers' chief sport was horse racing, and they had in their outfit one very fast Kentucky-bred animal and two or three others with a little speed, they thought it would be fun to race the Comanches. They had difficulty arousing the Indians' interest, but a quarter-mile race was finally arranged. An Indian brave came to the meeting place on what seemed to the cavalrymen one of the funniest little off-colored horses they had ever seen. They brought out their third best horse. The Indians bet buffalo skins and other possessions against flour, coffee, sugar, and bacon. The 170-pound Comanche carried a ridiculously heavy club which he swung about his head as he raced. The troopers roared with laughter, but their jaws soon dropped to open-mouthed wonder as the pony shot ahead of the cavalry horse and won. The troopers brought out their second-best horse and made more bets. The Comanche never changed horses or clubs. The outcome of the second race was the same as the first. Finally, the troopers brought out

their best mount, the Kentucky-bred racer. The Comanche threw away his club. At the start of the race he gave a war whoop. His pony jumped into the lead. As he drew near the finish line, with a comfortable distance between himself and the trooper, he reversed himself on his horse like a trick rider in a rodeo. Facing the losing racer, he beckoned to the soldier to catch up, but the soldier never did.

In the 1930s, Chief Quanah Parker of the Comanches owned a Palomino stallion named Bueno. A son of that stallion called Young Bueno sired a colt so fine that a white horseman bought it from the chief. He named it Desert Gold. One of Desert Gold's sons, Pirate Gold, is now famous in the pedigrees of present-day registered Palominos.

By the time the beauty of Chief Quanah Parker's colt was discovered by a white man, a few Californians had become fond of Palominos. The gold-colored horses were still considered too gaudy for horse shows, but they appeared in parades. Very few breeders of fine horses were interested in Palominos because they would not breed true. That is, when a Palomino is mated to a Palomino, the offspring is rarely a Palomino. The most usually successful way of getting a horse of true color was, and still is, to mate a Palomino with a sorrel (light chestnut). Nevertheless, one horsewoman of Pasadena, California, whose chief interest was competing in the Pasadena Rose Parade, bred Palominos. So few of her horses were off-color, not of golden body and white mane and tail, that many horsemen thought she had developed a true-breeding strain.

As Palominos began to find favor in California, an odd bit of good fortune helped to bring them into show ring respectability and recognition in the horse world. A rather silent man, without family and with few close friends but with a passionate fondness for the gold-colored horses, began to work to give the Palomino what he considered its rightful place. All that he ever revealed about himself was that he was born in Australia, but what he told and wrote about the golden horses impressed many horsemen. In magazine articles and pamphlets Dick Halliday told of the glory of Palominos in Baja, California, in the days of the Dons. He asserted that such horses were supreme gifts at weddings of the high born and at fiestas, and were the favorite mounts of the hidalgos, men descended from the nobility of Spain. He also maintained that many years ago one of the finest strains of horses in Arabia were all true Palomino color. Many of the Australian's historical "facts" were severely questioned, but by the time of his death (about 1945) in Florence, Arizona, the Palomino horse had its place among the favored breeds in America. Two Palomino associations with registries had been set up and Palomino classes were included in leading horse shows.

Of course, no one man is entirely responsible for the success of the Palomino, but the lonely Australian probably did more to bring the breed to public attention than any other man.

Following the Australian's lead, other authorities on horses brought forth facts, with somewhat more acceptable

proof, to advertise the virtues of the Palominos. One of the
authorities uncovered the record of a ride made in 1848
from Santa Fe, New Mexico, to Independence, Missouri, on
which the rider averaged 140 miles a day on the trip. His
favorite mount was a Palomino mare, Dolly. She covered
two hundred miles in twenty-six hours on that trip.

Hollywood helped in the rise of the Palomino. Few movie stars had more admirers than Trigger, Roy Rogers' Palomino. Many a movie was delayed, costing producers thousands of dollars, because no matter how close a guard was kept on Trigger at public appearances, he would emerge from them with a scraggly mane and tail. Fans could not resist the temptation of snipping off a lock of his hair, and the moviemaking would have to wait until Trigger grew more mane and tail!

Trigger was such a great animal, in intelligence as well as in other characteristics, that Rogers kept a band of twenty mares to mate him with in hopes of perpetuating his qualities.

Stand-ins were used for focusing cameras and other similar jobs on the set, but Trigger did his own running and acting. No trick photography was needed to fake his performances. He could lie down in bed and pull the covers over himself, back up to a chair and sit down in it, untie ropes, knock on a door, push a patient in a wheel chair gently down the corridor of a hospital, take a gun from a holster, drink from a bottle held in his teeth, pursue a calf while holding a rope in his teeth until he could drop the loop over the calf's head, and many other tricks—over fifty of them in all. This demonstration of intelligence helped to popularize the Palomino breed.

While the Palomino was coming into its own in the West, similar progress was afoot in the East. A dun horse, almost the same in coloring as the Palomino, was owned by a Pittsburgh lawyer, a man nearly as unusual as Dick Halliday. He was concerned about what he considered some foolish notions in the horse world. One of them was the idea that the Saddlebred Horse was just a show piece and not fit to participate in the United States Cavalry Annual Endurance Ride. Against the advice of officials and in spite of obstacles put in his way, he entered the contest with his American Saddle Horse, Rex Rysdyk. Rex made a perfect score. Then to prove that a saddler could be both show horse and using horse, the attorney showed Rex in leading horse shows of the East and won many first prizes with him.

Another attitude that the Pittsburgh lawyer wanted to challenge was the one that a Palomino was too gaudy to be a show horse. Rex Rysdyk had a full sister, Mystery. Mystery had a daughter, Sweet Campernelle, a perfectly golden Palomino. When that filly was a three-year-old, the lawyer could wait no longer. He took the mare to the greatest show for Saddlebred Horses in America, held annually at Louisville, Kentucky. There she won first place in her class. Then her owner took her to the National Horse Show in New York, the most proper and correct show in the United States, a show in which anything gaudy or otherwise in poor taste would be heavily discounted. Sweet Campernelle won four blue ribbons at that show and was also declared the Grand Champion!

By the time Sweet Campernelle became one of the top show horses in America, the two Palomino associations and their registries in the West were flourishing and registering Palominos all over the country. Sweet Campernelle's triumph gave other owners of Palomino-colored Saddlebreds the courage to show their horses. Soon Palominos were among the winners of three- and five-gaited classes in many of the major shows all across the nation. Breeders of American Saddle Horses of Palomino color formed an association and set up a registry.

In addition to their triumph in three- and five-gaited show rings, the golden horses also rose to fame in Quarter Horse circles. Sugar Simba, a Palomino, sold for a higher price than any other Quarter Horse at an annual Fort Worth Stock Show Quarter Horse Sale, bringing $10,200. Sword Play, a Palomino registered in the American Quarter Horse Registry, broke all track records at Turf Paradise in Phoenix, Arizona. Cutter Bill, another Palomino Quarter Horse, was named National Champion Cutting Horse of 1962.

The Appaloosa

Of all the breeds of odd color, perhaps of any color, the Appaloosa was the first to be bred with great skill in America. As early as 1720, the Nez Percé Indians were selecting their horses for breeding bands. They turned only their best stallions loose on the range, each with his band of selected mares. They divided their horses into four classes. One was the common kind used for trading with other tribes who found the carefully bred horses of the Nez Percé superior to those ridden by the white men. The second class was made up of pack horses and mounts for older men and women. The third class consisted of men's horses —not showy but very fast. The fourth class of horses was bred for buffalo hunting and for use as war horses.

The original home of the Nez Percé was ideal for horse breeding. In winter the snow did not become too deep in the sheltered valleys and in summer the high plateaus provided excellent grass. In the valleys and on the plateaus, horses were easily confined and protected from thieves and the intrusion of outside horses that might stray from other tribes or escape from white men.

The Nez Percé favored the Appaloosa horses because they liked their gay color. Viewed from afar, they blended into the scenery because of their natural camouflage. They also were fast, tough, and intelligent.

Fortunately, for the destiny of the Appaloosa, a segment of the Nez Percé Indians had separated from the main body of the tribe before Chief Joseph fled the harassment of the white man and headed his people for the Canadian border. He could not, of course, take all his herds with him. Some brood mares and a few stallions that were left behind were picked up by the Indians who stayed in the region of the Palouse River or were appropriated by ranchers. The Indians did not keep their horses long, for the missionary and his wife who came to teach them the new ways, at their request, felt that the gaudily colored horses were a bad influence on the Indians, keeping their minds and interest off toiling on their farms. Consequently, most of the Nez Percé disposed of their horses.

About 1875 when circuses and wild west shows arose in America, creating a demand for gaily colored horses, some Appaloosas were still to be found on the ranches and in a few Indians settlements of the Palouse River country.

The first trader to take advantage of the new demand for horses of fancy color did very well for himself. He took his pick of Appaloosas for about one hundred dollars a piece. Then he would match the horses in pairs and sell them for three thousand dollars or more a pair. One of his first buyers was Buffalo Bill's Wild West Show. The show traveled from coast to coast and gave the Appaloosas their first nationwide attention.

Most modern Appaloosas can trace their ancestry to a colt that was won in a poker game. A prospector searching for gold had an Appaloosa mare for a pack animal. One day when he was far from any town and just about out of grub for himself and grain for his mare, he stopped at a ranch house to ask if he could buy a little food and grain. In the corral he saw one of the finest stallions he had ever seen. With the usual range hospitality, he received the supplies he needed and moved on, but he could not get the fine stallion out of his mind. He made camp not many miles from the ranch and the next day he returned to bargain with the rancher. The prospector was anxious to mate the stallion with his Appaloosa mare. The colt that resulted from that mating of a half Thoroughbred stallion and a prospector's mare was a perfect Appaloosa—white with a black-spotted rump. The prospector dreamed of the fortune he would make from the races his colt would win when he grew up. But one night in town, with a little gold dust in his poke, he got into a poker game. He lost his gold dust and started to leave the saloon, but his companions jeered at him and called him a quitter, so he sat down again. A companion lent him money to open the game. When that was gone all he had left to bet on was his colt. The hand he held looked good so he bet the colt—and lost.

The rancher who won the colt named him Painter. Painter grew into a fine stallion, popular as a sire in his locality. He became known as Old Painter, the name he bears on some pedigrees today. One of his best sons was born to a black mare, the top animal of a famous rodeo string. The son was called Young Painter and he founded a line of Appaloosas that are highly valued today. A daughter of Old Painter is equally famous, though her fame came through her daughter. The famous daughter of Old Painter was bred to an Arabian stallion called Ferras. This mating resulted in a colt name Flash, a red roan with some gray and white in his coat and large, round dark spots on his rump.

The quality of the Old Painter line of Appaloosas was firmly fixed by what horsemen call "inbreeding" or "line breeding." To "fix the type" of a strain of horses means making sure that their sons, daughters, and future descendants will look and act much alike. To do this, closely related horses are mated. The type of the Painter family was fixed by mating a grandson and a granddaughter of Old Painter. The pair so mated was Flash and a daughter of Young Painter called Mystery. The colt that resulted from this mating was named El Zorro, Spanish for "The Fox." El Zorro grew up to became one of the most famous horses in Appaloosa history.

The man who bred and raised El Zorro developed the Painter line of Appaloosas. For many years he has been the president of the Appaloosa Horse Club, which keeps the register for Appaloosas. He crossed other types of horses with the original Painter line—Pintos, Palominos, and leopard spots. Later, he bought a registered Arabian stallion, a sorrel with a light mane and tail, to add refinement to his stock.

The Appaloosa breeders are constantly striving to improve the breed by selecting only the best animals for breeding and by bringing into the Appaloosa breed some Quarter Horse, Arabian, and Thoroughbred blood. Appaloosa color and other distinctive qualities of the breed are very strong. When a horse or mare of another breed and color is mated with an Appaloosa, the resulting foal is usually of Appaloosa color. Its feet are usually well formed and tough like those of its Appaloosa ancestors. The feet usually have the dark coloring with faint vertical lines peculiar to the Appaloosa.

Of course only animals that meet the requirements of the rules in the Appaloosa registry can be registered. Here is one of those rules:

> A horse must have a white rump starred with round or oblong spots and also flesh-colored spots around the eyes, nose, and genital organs. The stallions must be dominantly leopard spotted with white rump covered with dark spots. Any base color, such as gray, bay, chestnut, cream, white, roan, and so on, is acceptable.

The Appaloosa is winning respect and popularity today in many fields. Some win jumping classes in horse shows. Tinker Bell Day, a fine Appaloosa mare, was Reserve Champion Trail Horse of the West Coast. Handprint's High Chips, an Appaloosa, won the heavyweight division of a New Jersey 100-mile Endurance Ride.

These are but three of the many triumphs of Appaloosas in the fields of show jumping and trail-horse competition. As rodeo mounts and cutting horses they have been equally successful. State legislatures have granted the right of racing and parimutuel betting to Appaloosa breeders, a right formerly reserved for Thoroughbreds, Standardbreds, and Quarter Horses, and Appaloosa racing is drawing huge crowds in many states.

The Pinto or Paint

For many years, horsemen held a prejudice against the Pinto or Paint horse. Breeders and some ranchers held this prejudice very strongly. Perhaps it arose because many of the poorest of the Indian horses and wild horses were Pintos. There used to be a belief among horsemen that the Pinto color was the result of mixing breeds, but that has **been** proven false—unless, of course, one of the breeds in the "mix" is Pinto. In spite of the prejudice against him, "Old Paint" has been the hero of more western songs and stories than horses of any other color. "Strawberry Roan" and "Zebra Dun," though the ballads are well known, have only one song apiece. Most horsemen who have grown up in the West, whether they have a prejudice against the Pinto or not, can recall at least one "Old Paint" in their lives that was a favorite mount.

The history of the Pinto is closely connected with that

of the Appaloosa, though no Pinto horse can be registered
in the Appaloosa registry and no Appaloosa in the Pinto.
The color of the Paint or Pinto is in large and very definite
spots, a combination of white and any other color. The
Appaloosa looks as if someone had splattered a paint brush
at him—usually from behind, if his rump is basically white.
The history of the Appaloosa and Pinto started in China
many centuries ago, where gaily spotted horses were called

"heavenly horses." Persian tapestries and paintings show spotted horses. One picture many centuries old shows a polo game in which some of the horses are spotted. Because the best Spanish horses had Barb blood, and many of the Barb horses were Pintos, the conquistadors introduced Pintos to the New World.

The Pinto and other strikingly colored horses found great favor among the early settlers in Central and South America. The strikingly colored horses were favorite mounts on the great ranches from Mexico to Chile. In Spanish speaking countries they were called *Criollos*. Where Portuguese was the language, as in Brazil, *Crioulos* was the name. The Criollo, without human aid, had established itself as a kind of breed during the three hundred years after the first Spaniards brought over its Barb ancestors from Spain.

In 1920 a college professor in Buenos Aires selected and bred the foundation stock of modern Criollos in his country. He collected two thousand of the most typical Criollos he could find in the country. From them he selected fifteen mares and a few stallions to serve as the foundation stock for breeding.

In 1925 a Swiss teacher, a friend of the Buenos Aires professor, wanted "to see America from horseback." For him the professor selected two Criollos, eighteen and nineteen years old, to use as mount and pack horse for his ride. That ride from Buenos Aires to Washington D. C. was one of the toughest ever made by horses. It was 13,350 miles

long and led over some of the highest mountains and
broadest rivers in the world. It led through swamps at
sea level and below. Some of it was across deserts without
water. Mancha and Gato, the valiant Criollos that made
the 13,350-mile ride from Buenos Aires to Washington,
were returned to their native land by ship where they lived
at ease on the professor's ranch until they were both more
than thirty years old.

The visit of Mancha and Gato to Washington aroused
some interest in the breed among horsemen in the United
States. A few Criollos were imported by horsemen who
could afford the expense of shipping them from South
America. The Criollos, however, were not considered pretty
enough to suit North American tastes. Some of them, like
Gato, were attractively colored Pintos, but their heads were
not pretty. Most Criollos have Roman noses, like their Barb
ancestors, and their eyes are set high.

Though the interest in Pintos aroused by Gato and Mancha did not make Criollos popular in the United States, it
did cause North American horsemen to look around for
spotted horses that had pretty heads, arched necks, and
other attractive qualities. Men who had such horses began
to raise colts and develop a breed.

In the United States, the spotted-horse breed is known
as the Pinto. It does not include in its register any horse
not Pinto colored. The Criollo register, however, admits
solid duns, browns, and other colors if the individuals are

of Criollo blood and type. The Pinto Horse Association of America names as foundation sires two stallions. One is Sheik, a black and white Pinto, the other is Sun Cloud, a bay and white Pinto. Sheik's father was a Thoroughbred of solid color, but his mother was a Pinto called La Bernita. Her father was Two Step, a Pinto that was part American Saddle Horse and part Arabian. Sun Cloud's father was Sonny Boy, a champion parade horse, whose ancestors were mostly American Saddle Horses. Many of Sonny Boy's sons were champions in horse shows as pleasure horses.

There are many kinds of color patterns and combinations in the Pinto breed, but the rules of the register puts them into two classes. Here is what the rules say about color:

Pinto markings are divided into two patterns, Tobiano and Overo. These patterns are described: Tobiano—clearly marked pattern. White as a base with black, brown, sorrel, or dun as the other color. Markings distinct and the colors usually divided half and half. Mane and tail the color from which they stem. Legs white. Head dark or combined with star, snip, stripe, or blaze.

Overo—a colored horse, roan, dun, sorrel, bay, brown, or black, with white extending upward in irregular pattern. Mane and tail dark or mixed. Head usually white or bald. Legs have a combination of both colors.

Pintos are also described as "piebalds," "skewbalds," or paints. However, "piebalds" are black and white. Pintos and "skewbalds" are any other color BUT black Pintos.

The Arab

Two breeds of horses that were not developed in America but are highly prized by horsemen are the Thoroughbred, the most important and highest priced breed in America and many other lands, and the Arab. There is Thorough-bred blood in all American breeds because, in the early history of each of them, the parent or foundation stock was part Thoroughbred or some of their descendants were mated with Thoroughbreds and the results of those matings were included in the breed. In the same way, there is Arab blood in the Thoroughbred breed.

The Arab has the longest history of any breed of horse. It goes back in time so far that it is lost in legend. One of the oldest and best known legends goes like this:

Mohammed, the great prophet, wanted to select the best mares in Arabia. A great band of the finest that could be found were kept in stalls without water until they were very thirsty. The stables in which they were confined were near enough to a pond so the mares could smell water. When they were all turned loose from their stalls, of course they all ran at great speed toward the water. Just before they reached the pond, the command to halt was given. Only five mares obeyed the command. As thirsty as they were for water, they stopped in their tracks at the command and stood until the signal to go forward.

Mohammed, so the legend goes, proclaimed those five mares the greatest in the world and the source of all future *Asil* (noble) Arab horses. The five mares are said by some horsemen to be the foundation of the five great families of Arab horses. Whether the legend is true or not, it illustrates two facts about the Arab breed. First, the importance of the mare in a family or pedigree was considered much greater than that of the stallion. Families in American breeds are very often known only by the names of the stallions. In Arabia the family was known by the name of the mare. The second thing the story of Mohammed's mares illustrates is the importance placed upon intelligence and a good disposition in Arabia. Because of this regard for intelligence and a good disposition, only horses having these qualities were selected by Arabian breeders of fine horses.

The life of the Arabian people until modern times made the qualities of intelligence and amiability important to the user as well as to the breeder of horses. Most Arabians lived a nomadic existence. They moved about from place to place, making camp wherever they happened to be. Just

as the first white men in our own Southwest had to be on
the lookout for hostile Indians, so the Arabians had to be
on the lookout for hostile tribes. Whenever they camped,
they had to keep their horses nearby in case they were
needed against a surprise attack. Then too, any horse or
colt that strayed too far from camp might be stolen. So
the Arab horse became part of the family. The little foals
played with the children and sometimes came inside the
tents for indoor frolic. Children sometimes shared the milk
from a mare with her foal. To prevent theft at night, mares
were tethered to a stake by a locked iron shackle on one
leg. A less intelligent horse would certainly become hysteri-
cal and break a leg if so tethered. Of course, even an Arab
horse had to be taught to submit to such treatment when
he was a tiny foal.

The nomadic life of the Arab made necessary other qualities in the horse in addition to intelligence and a good
disposition. Until the development of modern military ma-
chinery, the horse was the most important weapon of war
in a country of deserts and mountains. When he made war
on an enemy tribe, the Arab would usually ride one of his
camels and lead his swiftest mare until he was near the
enemy. Then he would mount his mare and make the charge
into the enemy camp, dashing in and dodging about like a
fencer or making a quick run for his life in retreat. Indeed,
an Arabian's life was his horse. His horse had to be so
formed that it would stop more quickly than a modern
rope horse in a rodeo, spin around and jump sidewise or

backward. To do these things, a horse has to carry much of his own and his rider's weight on his hind legs. Sometimes he seems almost to squat on his hind feet. He can do so only if he has a strong short back and a flexible neck that will arch and bring the weight of his head directly over his shoulders. He cannot do this if his head is stuck out in front of him on a straight neck.

Because the Arab horse had to have a particular form or shape to perform his special job, the breed has a short powerful back, strong haunches, a flexible neck that arches easily, and shoulders that slope backward. With his fine, little muzzle he can eat dates out of a small bowl—sometimes the only food available—but for fast running or other quick action his nostrils can dilate until each is as large as a saucer. Also to give him breath for fast action, his windpipe is large, especially at the throat where it passes through his unusually wide jaws. His chest is not wide, for a horse whose forelegs are too wide apart will waddle like a duck and cannot run very fast. But the Arab's chest is very deep from top to bottom, giving him a lot of room for breath. His big eyes reflect his intelligence; there is room between them and above them for his large brain. His alert ears are set close together. The closely set ears, the delicacy of the nose, and the large amount of head between the eyes give the head of the Arab a diamond-shaped appearance when viewed from in front. His hoofs are tough and well formed. His legs just below the knees and hocks (the joints of the hind legs that look somewhat like your elbows) are short and shaped like an old-fashioned razor —broad when viewed from the side and very thin when viewed from the front. The part of the leg just above the knees and hocks is long and very muscular. Such legs and feet are, as horsemen know, the strongest kind and most suitable for the work the Arab war horse had to do.

When modern weapons of war changed methods of fighting, Arabians gradually stopped breeding their war horses. Fortunately, for the survival of the breed, a few of the best horses had been imported by some Polish noblemen.

one living near the border of Russia. The granddaughter of Lord Byron, the poet, went with her husband to Arabia about 1850 and selected some of the best remaining Arab horses to start England's most famous Arab breeding establishment, the Crabbet Stud. By a curious series of events the blood of one of the Polish collection of Arabs got to the Crabbet Stud.

The story of how Polish Arab horses got to England was told many years ago in an English magazine called *Country Life*. The story went like this:

After the great Revolution broke out in Russia and the Czar was overthrown, Red soldiers pillaged the great estates of the country, killing all livestock and burning buildings. As they ravaged the country along the border between Russia and Poland, they were not very careful about observing which side of the border they were on. They came upon a Polish estate on which some of the finest Arab horses in the world were bred. The Red soldiers hated, above all else, anything that was aristocratic. In their minds, anything of extremely fine quality was associated with the aristocracy. When they saw the Arab horses in the Polish stud, they immediately recognized their quality. To the soldiers these horses suggested aristocracy. So, instead of slaughtering them, they crucified some and burned others at the stake. Only two escaped. An old stableman who had spent his life with these fine animals managed to save two young stallions. With them he fled the country. No one knows what happened to one of the horses; but with the other, whose name was Skowronek, now famous in American pedigrees, the old man finally reached Paris, France. He could speak no language the French could understand and found no food or shelter for himself or his horse. They were both half starved by this time. By great good fortune, an English lady, daughter of the founders of the Crabbet Stud, happened to be in Paris and saw the half-starved horse and the old man. Instantly she recognized the rare quality of the horse and took both the old man and Skowronek back to England. Skowronek became a leading sire of the Crabbet Stud. Raffles, one of the most noted Arab sires in the

United States of America, was foaled by a mare and sired by a stallion, both descended from Skowronek. Several sons of Skowronek became famous sires in the United States.

Long before the sons and daughters of Skowronek came to America, Arab horse blood had been cherished here and the breed was recognized, though it was not nearly as popular as it has become today. Before the Arab breed was established in America, a few wealthy Americans imported Arabs. Also, as more frequently happened, a foreign prince would honor a distinguished American by giving him an Arab horse as a present. In the late 1800s such a prince presented a Kentucky colonel with a fine Arab stallion named Zilcadi. The names of the prince and of the Kentucky colonel are forgotten, but many an owner of an American Saddle Horse points proudly to the imported Zilcadi on his horse's pedigree. Benjamin's Whirlwind, Zilcadi's son, was one of the famous sires of the American Saddle Horse breed. A daughter of Zilcadi was mated with Vermont Morgan. The colt from that mating became one of the most famous trotting horses in the world. His name was Goldust. One of his daughters, Goldust Maid, broke all the trotting records of the world when she was eighteen years old!

Not all the names of Americans receiving horses as tokens of honor from foreign rulers are forgotten. William H. Seward, Secretary of State under Abraham Lincoln, received an Arab horse as a present from a Syrian official; President Polk received another; and Ulysses S. Grant, while President of the United States, was sent two of the finest Arabian horses from the stables of the Sultan of Turkey. Their names were Leopard and Linden Tree. They were crossed with daughters of Henry Clay, a famous American trotting horse and a great-grandson of an Arab horse, and had some very fine foals.

Breeders of Arab horses in the United States now have an association and registry. Within the past few years the popularity of Arab horses has increased greatly. Their ability to get along with people, to be "one of the family" as they were in the days of their early history in Arabia, makes them a favorite. Because of their beautiful appearance, they are popular as show horses. They are used by horse raisers of the new breeds of striking color to improve the quality of the breeds. Though Arabs are always of solid color, with now and then some white on the face or legs, when they are mated with a gaily colored horse their offspring frequently has the color of the non-Arab parent. So there are many half-Arab Palominos, Pintos, and Appaloosas.

Some of the best Arabs are now raised in Poland, where they are used exclusively for racing. Many Polish Arabs have recently been imported by American breeders. There is also a movement under way to import Arabs from the stables of Egypt. Some of them are even better than those of Poland. The importations from Poland and Egypt have led to the start of Arab racing in the United States, where tracks for racing under saddle are confined to use by Thoroughbreds—with some Quarter Horse races permitted.

However, Arab breeders are starting to build their own tracks or to get certain days set aside for them at existing tracks, just as the Appaloosa breeders are doing. Arabs cannot run a mile or a quarter mile as fast as Thoroughbreds or Quarter Horses, but such attractive little animals are sure to draw crowds at any track.

The Thoroughbred

Thoroughbreds are the fastest breed of horses in the world. Every year they win millions of dollars in prizes on race tracks in the United States. Many more millions of dollars are bet yearly at those tracks. Now and then, a Thoroughbred race horse sells for over a quarter of a million dollars.

Thoroughbred is the name of the breed. People who do not know anything about horses sometimes think the word means the same as purebred. To a horseman it does not. If you should say to a horseman that you saw a beautiful Thoroughbred Palomino, he would be either amused or

sorry for your ignorance. To speak of a Thoroughbred Palomino, or Thoroughbred of any other breed, is like speaking
of a collie bulldog.

When Henry VIII was King of England, there were many
kinds of horses in the stables of the aristocrats and in the
royal stable of the King. A list of the horses in the stable
of Henry VIII includes several animals of the Great Horse
breed, from which come the draft horses like the Clydesdale
and Shires. The list also includes "chargers," big horses
used for carrying knights in heavy armor, pack horses of
no particular breed, and Hobbies, the popular little easy-
riding horses developed in Ireland and widely used in
England.

While the Hobbies, the Galloways, and other small, easy-
gaited breeds were the most popular mounts, the most
fashionable and high-priced, up until the time of the Crusades, were the Great Horses. The Crusades changed the
fashion of horse breeding in England. The knights in armor
on their big horses were no match for their enemy. It is
written in an old book: "The Infidels not being weighed
down with heavy armour like our knights but always able
to outstrip them in pace, were a constant trouble. When
charged they are wont to fly, and their horses are more
nimble than any others in the world; one may liken them
to swallows for swiftness."

The few Englishmen who could afford to do so imported
Turkish, Barb, and Arabian horses. These importations were
crossed with the native horses of England. The best results

were obtained by crossing them on the smaller ones. This bringing in of Oriental blood and crossing it on native stock did not progress very far when England was torn by revolution, and horse breeding almost came to a standstill. Some horse breeding was carried on and the sport of horse racing started. It continued even under Oliver Cromwell, though racing was illegal while he ruled England.

During the Puritan Revolution and rule in England, the exiled king, Charles II, lived in France, where he became an excellent horseman and adopted French taste in horses. The French had imported Oriental horses and developed strains of beautiful, elegant, fast horses. When Charles finally became King of England, he wanted to establish a breed of English horses as elegant and fast as those of France. He ordered his good friend, the Duke of Newcastle, to assemble a band of twenty mares to be used as the start of such a breed. This selection of mares to start a breed was unusual in England, where breeding is, and has always been, reckoned through the stallions. Perhaps Charles or Newcastle had learned some of the wisdom of the Orient, where the breeding of a horse is reckoned by the mares from which the horse has descended. Whatever the reason for the selection of the band of mares, they were assembled in the king's stable and called the Royal Mares. From then on, a horse descended from them and the stallions in the king's stables was called "thoroughbred." Great argument still goes on about the breeding of those mares. Some horsemen claim they were all of Oriental (Arabian, Barb, Spanish, and Turkish) blood. However, the most reliable records show that some of them had the blood of the little native English horses in their veins.

Great though the influence of those mares was on the development of English horses, credit is given today to four stallions for being the foundation of the English Thoroughbred. Certainly to the blood of those four stallions and the Royal Mares, the Thoroughbred owes the beauty and the elegance he had before he began to be selected and bred for speed without regard for any other quality. Even today, we occasionally see a Thoroughbred with the big, low-set eyes, delicate little nose, beautiful neck, and elegant carriage so admired by early breeders of Thoroughbreds. Such animals show the influence of Oriental blood most strikingly. However, the great speed of the Thoroughbred could not have been achieved without the homely little horse native to England. When the first Oriental horses were brought to England, they were raced against the native English horses. Like the American cavalry officers who raced their Kentucky horse against the homely little Comanche pony, the owners of the imported horses were put to shame. However, when the blood of the native English horses was mixed with the blood of the Oriental imports, faster horses than had ever before been seen were the result. Such is the mystery and fascination of horse breeding.

The four great Oriental stallions now considered the founders of the English Thoroughbred were all imported into England in the first half of the century in which the

American Colonies revolted against England. Within a few years after their being established as sires in England, only horses who descended from them through their fathers or the male members of their father's family (that is, whose grandfathers were sons of one or more of the four foundation stallions) could be called Thoroughbreds. Even today, every Thoroughbred in England and America traces his ancestry through his male ancestors to those four stallions. They were the Byerly Turk, the Darley Arabian, the Godolphin Barb, and Alcock Arabian.

By the time the four Oriental stallions had established themselves as heads of their breed in England, Americans had developed at last one breed, the Narragansett Pacer, and several strains or families of horses such as the Cockspurs and Chickasaws. The foundation of those families was almost entirely the little, easy-gaited horses so popular in England before the Thoroughbred breed was established. There was some Dutch and French blood in that stock and, in the Chickasaws, some Indian pony blood. The early colonial horses were valued for their easy riding quality, for their endurance, and for their ability in racing. The racing was usually competition between two horses over a short distance, about a quarter of a mile.

By the time the American Revolution was over, Thoroughbreds in England were being bred for hunting and for racing. Both of the sports had become very popular there. Soon the most aristocratic colonists, those who lived in Virginia, took up the British fashion of fox hunting and also began to develop race tracks. They imported English Thoroughbreds for both hunting and racing. The early Thoroughbred races in this country were four miles long and were often very cruel affairs. Sometimes a horse would race three "heats," each one four miles long, in one day; and the winning horse would average over thirty miles an hour. It was not uncommon for a horse to drop dead during a race. Often a winning horse would end the race bleeding from spur cuts and whip lashings.

Most of the Thoroughbreds imported by the Virginians were descended from three English Thoroughbreds. One, named Eclipse, was a great-great-grandson of the Darley Arabian. Another of the English horses from which American Thoroughbreds descended was Herod, great-great-grandson of the Byerly Turk; still another was Matchem, grandson of the Godolphin Barb (also called the Godolphin Arabian). Janus, another grandson of the Godolphin Barb, became a famous sire. His fame came from his sons, owned, not by the Virginia aristocrats, but by the backwoods farmers. Those sons in the backwoods were not Thoroughbreds: they were Quarter Horses.

Janus was a stocky little sorrel with a narrow strip in his face. He had one white hind foot and a speckled rump. The coloring of his rump passed on to at least one of his famous descendants, Bloody Buttocks, noted sire in the Quarter Horse registry. Appaloosas are now being bred to his descendants and most of them are perfect Appaloosas in color. Janus won a few four-mile races. In one of them he beat a horse imported from England by a member of the family of William Byrd of Virginia.

Though Janus won a few four-miles races, his colts were not generally good four-mile horses. However, many farmers had brought their mares to the little horse owned by an aristocrat and had raised colts that won races on the short dirt tracks in the backwoods. Because of his failure as a sire of four-mile horses he was sold to a Carolina farmer. He was resold many times. For nineteen years, he continued to be used as a sire of quarter-mile race horses and had thousands of sons and daughters. His fame became so great that the Virginia aristocrats wanted him back. When Janus was thirty-four years old a Mr. John Goode of Mecklenburg, Virginia, offered a large sum of money for the old stallion to be delivered to his stable. The game little horse was started on the long journey one cold winter day. He got as far as the stable of a Colonel Haynes in Warren County, North Carolina, but could go no farther. There he died. Today he lives on in the hearts of southwestern horsemen and is known by many as "the father of the Quarter Horse." Almost all the famous Quarter Horses whose pedigrees are known and who show some Thoroughbred blood are descendants of Janus.

Among the earliest of English Thoroughbreds imported to the colonies were two mares, Queen Mab and Selima. The most famous of the earliest stallions were Bully Rock (also spelled Bulle Rock), Spark, Traveller, Othello, Fearnaught, and Messenger, probably the most noted Thoroughbred sire to be imported. One of Messenger's grandsons, American Eclipse, was never beaten in a race. At nine years of age Eclipse carried 127 pounds to win a four-mile match race. His opponent, Sir Henry, was a four-year-old and carried only 108 pounds.

Messenger was the sire of many of the most famous horses in America. One of them was the sire of Hambletonian 10.

Ninety per cent of all the Standardbred horses of America are descendants of Hambletonian 10.

The great Thoroughbreds imported by the colonists were mated to each other's offspring and to the best of the animals of the old American families. They were used for racing and fox hunting.

The first registry record for American Thoroughbreds was called the American Stud Book. It was set up by Sanders D. Bruce in 1873. By 1896 the most important men associated with racing in America had formed an organization called the Jockey Club. In that year the Club bought the American Stud Book from Mr. Bruce. Since 1896 the name of every registered American Thoroughbred has been recorded in that book.

English Thoroughbred breeders claimed that American Thoroughbreds had too much "cold blood" (blood of horses other than Thoroughbreds) and refused to register any

American horse whose ancestors were not registered in the English stud book. This refusal to accept American blood has become an embarrassment to the English. Some of the greatest American race horses, ones that defeated the best English horses on American tracks, cannot be entered in the English stud book. Of course, the English would like to have colts from the winning American horses, but they cannot do so because they cannot register them in their stud book and therefore cannot race them on their Thoroughbred tracks. One of the great American horses that cannot be entered in the English stud book was Man o' War!

American Thoroughbreds are, of course, best known as race horses. They are also used as hunters and as jumpers in horse shows, sometimes performing over jumps seven feet high. They are the favorite mounts of competitors in Olympic contests and are used in all the leading polo matches. American dressage riders use Thoroughbreds for performing the movements made famous by the Lippizan horses of the Vienna Riding School.

One of the most important uses of American Thoroughbreds is in crossing on other breeds to improve the quality of those breeds. As we have seen, ninety per cent of American Standardbreds are descendants of Messenger. American Eclipse, Bloody Buttocks, and other famous Thoroughbreds are on the pedigree of Denmark, who was named foundation sire of the American Saddle Horse. Palomino, Pinto, and Appaloosa breeders are continually using Thoroughbred crosses to improve the quality of their stock.

The appearance of the Thoroughbred has changed some
since the time he was first imported into the colonies. At
that time he usually had a beautiful head with large, low-set
eyes, and dainty muzzle. His neck was long, flexible, and
naturally arched. Today, after many generations of selective
breeding for speed, with little attention to any other quality,
he is slightly different. The speedy horse sticks his neck out
in front of him on a straight neck so his weight is mostly on
his forelegs, leaving his hind legs to push his body forward
in great leaps, over twenty feet at a stride, when he is running
his fastest. The larger his nostrils, the better for taking in
air. The desire to run is more important than intelligence.
Consequently, today some Thoroughbreds are excitable and
hard to control. Their heads sometimes have little brain
room above the eyes and are not quite as pretty as in Revolutionary days. Some of them have necks that are straight
and a bit stiff in appearance. But they always have a racy
look like that of a greyhound, the deep chests, and the
fine legs.

Now and then one of today's Thoroughbreds displays the
beauty and elegance of the horses of Charles II. Man o' War
was such an animal. When he was a yearling he was thought
to be too pretty to run fast. Others said he looked too much
like an American Saddle Horse. Mr. Riddle, who owned
Man o' War until the horse died at the age of thirty years,
bought him for five thousand dollars, a very low price for a
yearling of his breeding. Even though intelligence is not the
most important characteristic in a race horse, it has not died

out of the breed. In rodeos and ranches of the West, there are many Thoroughbreds today doing work that takes the most intelligent and responsive kind of horse. The word Thoroughbred is still the most highly respected one in the minds of many American horsemen.

Index